Let's Think!

Philosophical stories to stimulate thinking

WGHS Junior School

Written by
PAUL CLEGHORN and STEPHANIE BAUDET

First Published
February 02 in Great Britain by

PUBLISHING

© **Paul Cleghorn and Stephanie Baudet 2002**

The moral right of the author has been asserted in accordance with the
Copyright, Designs and Patents Act 1988

A CIP record for this work is available from the British Library

ISBN-10: 1-900818-13-2
ISBN-13: 978-1-900818-13-1

Typeset by Educational Printing Services Limited

Educational Printing Services Limited
Unit 6, Glenfield Park 2, Northrop Avenue, Blackburn BB1 5QH
Telephone: (01254) 686500   Fax: (01254) 686501
Email: enquiries@eprint.co.uk   Website: www.eprint.co.uk

It is our light, not our darkness that most frightens us.

We ask ourselves, who am I to be brilliant, gorgeous, talented, and fabulous?

Actually, who are you not to be?

You are a child of God. Your playing small doesn't serve the world.

There's nothing enlightened about shrinking so that other people won't feel insecure around you.

We were born to make manifest the glory of God that is within us.

It's not just in some of us; it's in everyone.

As we let our own light shine, we unconsciously give other people permission to be the same.

Nelson Mandela
1994 Inaugural Speech

---

*Let's give children permission to shine,
and empower them to do so!*

Introduction

This book has principally been written to provide stories for assemblies in the primary school. They have been written in groups of themes, using classical, philosophical ideas. They are designed to stimulate thinking and discussion, and to engage the children in realising how the understanding of such issues affects their own lives.

The stories can also, usefully, be used in the classroom, especially with a 'community of enquiry' method as advocated by proponents of Philosophy for Children. Most usefully, a story that has been introduced in the context of an assembly, can be further developed in the classroom.

In 'Thinkers of the East', Idries Shah tells of someone who once complained to a Sufi *(a sect within the Islamic tradition)* sage that the stories which he told were interpreted in different ways by different people. 'That is precisely their value', he said; 'surely you would not think much of a cup from which you could drink water but not milk, or a plate from which you could eat meat but not fruit? A cup and plate are limited containers - how much more should language be to provide nutrition? The question is not, 'How many ways can I understand this?', or 'Why can I not see it in only one way?' The question is, 'Can this individual profit from the stories'.

We hope that children can profit from these stories in many different ways.

How To Use This Book:

There are five stories on each of ten themes.

The ten themes are:

- ❑ **Happiness**
- ❑ **Goodness**
- ❑ **Service**
- ❑ **Beauty**
- ❑ **Patience**
- ❑ **Knowledge**
- ❑ **Wisdom**
- ❑ **Justice**
- ❑ **Myself**
- ❑ **Truth**

If daily assemblies are held, each theme corresponds to a week's work, and therefore provides some continuity and progression. Alternatively, single stories, or a small group can be used in 'pick-n-mix' fashion. Anyone who has taken even a few assemblies knows that each individual feels more comfortable with some stories and themes than with others, so the wide variety provided gives plenty of scope for choice. The best advice is not to talk about something you are not comfortable with - children are not that stupid - they'll find you out!

Some schools use prayers within the assembly, whilst others do not. Prayers have not been included because the best prayers are those which arise to meet the need of the moment, not those which are set down and then repeated, whether they are apt or not. If necessary, the 'Thought for the Day' can be turned into a prayer.

We have tried to provide some variety in including some traditional stories from different cultures as well as new, original stories. Some are in narrative and some in dialogue, with a few written as plays where pupils can at least read the parts, if not fully enact the drama. The most important aspect is not the story, but rather the thinking and subsequent engagement of the pupils immediately following the story. For this, we rely on you, the reader and 'facilitator' in the assembly, but we offer some 'tips' and advice as to how this might be made most effective.

❑   It is envisaged that assemblies formulated from material contained in this book will be active, with as much pupil participation as possible - not an easy task, especially in a large school. Remember that engagement also means mental engagement - in the context of an assembly only a certain number of children can speak. However, a good assembly which gets children thinking, will be much more effective than one in which the children are passive and receive a 'message' with no challenge to engage with it.

❑   Use the well-known story telling strategies, such as telling the story, rather than reading it. Use 'props' and visual aids as much as possible, to develop a multi-sensory approach. Use a few pupils to help you, perhaps by miming the story if it's quite short. If you do have to read the story but the language is 'not you', then change it as you read.

❑   Don't be afraid to give 'thinking time' even in an assembly. Allow children a short time to consider a story and its meaning, and, if necessary, focus their attention with a couple of questions first.

❑   The skill of the questioner is crucial to aiding understanding, and although a small number of questions are given as ideas, don't let them be limiting - follow any appropriate leads from the children. A range of types of questions are given in appendix A.

❑   Don't *(I mean DON'T)* ask all the questions for the sake of finishing. If any interaction has come to the end of its natural life, quit while you're ahead!

CONTENTS

CONTENTS

Happiness

What is happiness? The question forms the essence of this section, and is also said to be one of the essential questions in life. We all want to be happy, and in society we see happiness being pursued in multifarious ways. The stories in this theme illustrate that happiness is something that is discovered 'within', rather than 'without'. It is discovering, through self-knowledge, that in effect we choose to be happy. In truth, happiness proves not to be related to possessions or position, as many believe. We see those around us who are happy in almost all *(some would say all)* situations, and those who are miserable no matter what their circumstance! One survey in 2001 showed that the people of Bangladesh, an extremely poor nation materially, came out top in the 'happiness stakes' - the percentage of those surveyed who considered themselves happy!

> *'My daily affairs are quite ordinary;*
> *But I'm in total harmony with them.*
> *I don't hold on to anything, don't reject anything*
> *Nowhere an obstacle or conflict.*
> *Who cares about wealth or honour?*
> *Even the poorest things shine.*
> *My miraculous power and spiritual activity:*
> *Drawing water and carrying wood'.*

P'ang Yun
Zen master in ancient China

Perhaps at first sight contradictory, the stories also show that despite happiness being found within, the individual has to 'move out' or 'open out' to find it. In other words it is not to do with being introverted or self-centred but with opening up to people, places and events. To being in the present moment.

Happiness was once described as a by-product; a mode of travelling, not a station at which one arrives. *'Happiness is like chasing a butterfly. The more you chase it and chase it directly, then it will just elude you. If you sit down quietly and turn your thoughts to other things then the butterfly will softly come and sit upon your shoulder'.*

Dr Murray Banks
Psychiatrist

When a desire for something is satisfied (i.e. we get the desired object), that desire goes immediately and is usually replaced by another one. In the minds of many of us, happiness is associated with the satisfying of the desire - but of course, experience shows that happiness is just as ethereal as the desire! In this story, Jenny no sooner achieves one desire than she replaces it with another.

Jenny's Skates

'Hi, Jenny!' said Narinder, grinning. 'I got some ice skates in the holidays. White leather ones. You know the new rink is open? I'm going to learn figure skating'.

Jenny dumped her schoolbag on the floor and sat down. 'I got the new Gary Haines CD', she said.

'I want to get that CD, too', said Narinder. 'Are you getting some skates?'

Jenny shrugged, trying to look as if she didn't care. 'You can hire them at the rink'.

Narinder pulled a face. 'Yeah, but it's better to have your own, isn't it, Con?'

The boy next to her nodded. 'Do you think you'll be getting some, Jen?'

'Yes', said Jenny, with more conviction than she felt. She really wanted skates. More than anything else in the world. But they were expensive. Jenny loved watching the skating on TV, especially the ice dance. That was the best.

'Let's go on Saturday', said Conrad. 'Do you think you'll have your skates by then, Jen?'

'Maybe', said Jenny. She would ask her mum when she got home. To have a pair of skates of her own would be great. Surely Mum would see how happy it would make her?

'We're going skating on Saturday', she announced when she got home. 'The new rink is open'.

'How much is it?' asked her mother.

'Two pounds'.

1

'What about hiring skates?'

Jenny hesitated. 'I wondered if you'd buy me a pair - now that you're working. All my friends are getting them. Narinder got some during the holidays . . .'

'Jennifer, I can't afford it'.

'There might be some second hand ones in the paper', said Jenny, hopefully.

'When are you getting your skates?' asked Narinder the next day, clattering her chair down off the table, as usual.

'Mum's going to look in the paper for some good second hand ones'.

Narinder sniffed.

Conrad came in. He'd brought his skates to school to show everyone. They were made of smooth, black leather and the new blades gleamed. He put them on and wobbled about the classroom.

'You'll blunt the blades', said Narinder. 'I'm not allowed to walk in mine, even with the guards on'.

Conrad wasn't allowed to walk in his for long, either. Mrs Holson came in and told him to take them off, immediately.

'Did you find any skates in the paper?' Jenny asked her mum when she got home.

'You'll have to hire some', said her mother, shaking her head. 'Perhaps you could have some for your birthday if you're still keen. We'll see'.

'Oh Mum!' wailed Jenny. Her birthday wasn't until August. 'It's not fair! I don't want to hire skates! Everyone else has their own'.

'Then you'll not have to go', said Mum, 'and that's the end of it'.

Jenny stomped upstairs to her room and slammed the door. She lay down on the bed with her head to the wall. How could she face her friends on Saturday, in hired skates, when she'd said she was getting some?

To her relief, ice skates were not mentioned again until Friday, at home time.

'We're meeting at the rink at two o'clock', said Conrad, swinging his bag over his shoulder. 'Don't forget to bring your skates. See yer'.

Jenny tried to tell him. She opened her mouth to say, 'I haven't got any skates. I'm not getting any skates', but Conrad had pushed through the doors and was gone.

She got there, early, bought her ticket and went to the skate hire counter, fumbling with her ticket.

'What size?' asked the man.

'Three please'.

'Give us your shoes then'.

Jenny bent down to take off her trainers and put them on the counter. The man was scanning the shelves behind him. He shook his head.

'Sorry, no threes left. Must be a popular size. We've got more on order'.

Jenny stared at her trainers on the counter but did not pick them up. How could they run out of skates?

'Hang on', said the man, turning back to the shelf. 'Here, borrow these. They're second hand ones which we're selling for someone. Twelve quid if you want to buy them, and don't tell anyone I lent them to you'.

Jenny reached for the skates. They were white leather. She ran her thumb carefully across the double blade. Just what she wanted. If only she had twelve pounds.

Then she had an idea. She grabbed the skates, with a grateful grin to the man, and went to look for her friends.

'Narinder!' she shouted. Breathlessly, she caught up with them at the changing room door. 'Narinder, you know that Gary Haines CD? What will you give me for it?'

Narinder turned, in surprise, and then looked down at the skates in her hand. 'Why? Do you need some money?'

Jenny nodded. 'I need twelve pounds. I've got four from Christmas and Mum's change here that I'll borrow. I still need a fiver, though'.

'Done', said Narinder.

Jenny grinned, happily, as they went to put their skates on. She had her own pair of skates at last! FANTASTIC!

The three friends went skating nearly every Saturday for a while, but then the other two began making excuses not to go. There were other things they wanted to do. Conrad joined the local Under Twelve's football team and Narinder had started going into town shopping with her older sister. Jenny still enjoyed skating and had become quite good and there were still people she knew who went, but she decided she didn't want to be an ice dancer after all.

One thing she really would like was a drum kit. There was a girl drummer in Gary Haines' band . . .

End

Questions

1. Can you think of a time when you really wanted something but couldn't have it? *(Ask for examples).*

2. Ask two or three children why they wanted the particular thing they did.

3. What does it feel like to really want something?

4. How did you expect to feel once you had it? *(Directing the question to children who have answered).*

5. Did it happen? Did you feel like you expected to? Did the feeling last? How long? A day . . . a week . . . a month . . . forever? *(Again directing to particular children).*

Thought for the Day:

It is nice to get things, but getting things doesn't make us happy for very long – we soon want something else. We should look to see what it is that makes us really happy.

Wallace wants to be famous, but he's not quite sure how to achieve it - although he doesn't really care! Being famous - that's the thing - if only he can become famous he'll be really happy . . . or will he?

Wallace's Dream

Wallace picked his way over the dunes and tufts of grass until he reached the beach. Would this be the day when his dream came true?

He loved the early morning. Quiet except for the gentle swish of the waves breaking over the sand and the occasional gull, screaming, overhead. There were never many people on this beach. It was far from the town or any main roads. A secret, really. A secret paradise. Yet this morning, as usual, Wallace thought about his dream. To become famous.

He'd had the dream for as far back as he could remember. His life was so ordinary. He could see it stretching in front of him, year after year, unchanging, and when he died it would be as if he had never existed. No-one would remember him.

Wallace longed for excitement. He wanted to be somebody. His name in the paper, to be recognised in the street, to be envied by others. But how all this was going to happen, he didn't know.

Perhaps he had a hidden talent for painting, or writing. Perhaps he would be discovered and become a film actor or a pop singer. Maybe he would find something washed up on the beach. Treasure from a sunken galleon or the bones of a dinosaur.

As he walked he kept his eyes on the sand but there was nothing but seaweed.

He reached the outcrop of rocks which marked the end of this little beach and sat down. He'd brought his silver flute with him, as usual, and he began to play.

Suddenly, a movement made him look up.

A girl sat watching him. She was perched on a rock several metres out to sea.

'Don't stop', she said. 'I do love music'.

She was pale with long, fair hair and she sat with her legs dangling . . .

5

Wallace blinked and then squinted, the sun in his eyes. Her legs seemed to catch the light and sparkle in many facets. Strange.

'I didn't see you arrive', he said, sliding off the rock and walking towards her.

She smiled, shyly, and half turned away from him towards the sea. But not before he had seen that instead of legs she had the pearly scales of a fish's tail.

She was a mermaid!

After that, she often came to hear Wallace play his flute and she would tell him tales of life under the sea and ask him what it was like to be a human being. For a while he forgot his desire for fame in the excitement of her company. He sat, spellbound, by her words of wisdom and insight into life.

'Are you happy?' she asked him, one day.

'Happy?' he answered, and was surprised that he couldn't reply, immediately.

'Do you understand what happiness is?' she asked.

He thought for a moment, sat on the rock beside her. 'Being content, knowing what you want out of life?' he said.

She smiled. 'And do you know what you want?'

'Oh yes'. There was no hesitation now. There was no stopping him. He told her about his dream of fame and recognition and she listened, watching him with her clear blue eyes.

It was later that he realised just how his dream could come true and the next morning, when he went to the beach, he took his camera with him.

'I'm going to take your photo', he explained. 'An image of you will come out on a piece of paper'.

'But, you can see me', said the mermaid, 'why do you want me on a piece of paper?'

Wallace smiled. 'So that I can remember you and know that you're real'.

The next morning, Wallace was not alone when he went to the beach. With him was a photographer from the local newspaper, who made jokes about mermaids and laughed loudly as they walked.

The mermaid was shy and refused to come close. She sat with her back to them on the furthest rock from the beach. The photographer was unconvinced but clicked his camera and went away grumbling about not having got a clear picture.

Nevertheless, a picture of the mermaid appeared in the paper at the weekend and Wallace smiled with satisfaction and cut out the article. There he was, on the front page!

But not many people would see it, and by next week something else would make the headlines. Wallace had other plans.

When he saw the mermaid again he showed her the paper. 'This week we were in the local paper but tomorrow the National Press are coming. We can be famous, both of us. No-one has ever photographed a mermaid before, in fact, not many people even believe in them'.

'You can believe in me', she retorted. 'You can see me'.

'But no-one else will believe it', insisted Wallace.

'If that will make you happy', she said, her voice low and sad.

When the National Press came, with a reporter and a photographer, she allowed them a better picture with Wallace as well. This picture made the front page too but this time people all over the country could read it.

Other papers and magazines began phoning Wallace, in fact, the phone never stopped ringing, even as early as six o'clock in the morning. He was so busy that he often didn't have time for his usual quiet walks along the beach and he missed them.

When he did meet the mermaid again, he said, 'The TV people are coming on Friday. Then I'll be famous all around the world'.

Soon, Wallace's diary was full with requests for interviews and appearances on chat shows. He was asked to give talks about the mermaid and a publisher asked him to write a book. His photo with the mermaid appeared everywhere and people began to recognise him in the street and ask for his autograph.

Wallace revelled in it all.

Still, when he could, he took his silver flute and went down to the beach in the early mornings to play and talk to the mermaid. But she came less and less.

There were nearly always people on his strip of beach now, hoping for a glimpse of her. They parked their cars and their caravans along the quiet lane and ran, noisily, down to the beach, cameras at the ready.

They left their litter on the clean sand and chalked graffiti on the rocks.

When the mermaid didn't appear they knocked on his door, demanding he call her, or mobbed him if he ventured outside.

Wallace was famous all right. He was rich, too, from all the high fees paid for his appearances. But finally a 'For Sale' notice appeared outside his house. His quiet beach had gone.

No longer could he enjoy the serenity and the bird song in the early morning on his stroll along the beach. No longer could he sit on the rock and play his flute while the gentle waves surged onto the sand. He longed for that time to come back again.

That time, when he was truly happy.

End

Questions

1. Has anyone ever wanted to be famous? Tell us about it. *(Take two or three examples)*.

2. Who is your favourite, famous person?

3. Do you think famous people are happy? What is your evidence? Opposite views? What is the evidence?

4. Is fame anything to do with happiness? What makes you think so?

5. How did Wallace's views of happiness change?

Thought for the Day:

Wallace thought that being famous would make him happy, but it only made him miserable. We can all be happy just the way we are, so look to see what it is that makes you happy.

8

Melanie and Dan have been looking forward to a surprise holiday. Like many of us, there is the expectation of having a happy time when they get there. Melanie and Dan's Mum and Dad have a different sort of holiday in mind, which serves to show that it's important to be happy all the time and not have the notion that it is exclusive to special events.

Are We There, Yet?

'Are we there, yet?' asked Melanie, sighing. 'I'll be really happy when we're there'. She stared out of the car window. Motorways were boring.

Dad laughed. 'We've only just set off. Be patient, Melanie. Why don't you both play some of those games we bought?'

Melanie had forgotten about them. She brightened and looked at her brother Daniel.

'Shall we, Dan?'

He shrugged. 'OK'.

Melanie delved into her 'Tote' bag. She didn't really know where they were going on holiday. Mum and Dad hadn't said, exactly.

'You'll see', they said. That phrase always made her grit her teeth with frustration. It was like when Gran said she would take them somewhere or buy them something, and then added: 'All being well'. Melanie hated anything vague, she liked everything to be definite.

For a while she and Daniel played some of the games in the pack, which was called: 'Games to Play on Long Journeys'.

The next time she looked out of the window she recognised the road.

'We're at Auntie Maureen's and Uncle Max's house!' she said.

'Great', said Daniel, gathering his things together. They always enjoyed seeing their cousins.

They spent three days there but then it was into the car again.

'So we're not there, yet?' said Daniel. 'I thought that was our holiday. It was great, but I'll be happy when we really get there'.

9

Later that morning the weather became very hot and about eleven o'clock they drew into a big parking area and found a space.

'Swimming costumes', said Mum. 'And don't forget your towels'.

'Water World', read Melanie, looking at the huge letters over the entrance.

It was great fun. Soon they were diving into waves made by the wave machine and swirling down a water chute on an inflated ring. There was a water helter-skelter and a man-made river with rapids, where you ended up under a waterfall.

They had lunch in the cafeteria and spent the afternoon in the water again. That night they stayed in a nearby Bed and Breakfast.

'Can we go to Water World again tomorrow?' asked Daniel, as he climbed into bed.

Mum nodded. 'If it's fine', she said, and Melanie gritted her teeth under the bedclothes.

It was fine and hot the next day so they stayed at the water park.

In the car the following morning, Melanie said, 'Now, where are we going? Aren't we there, yet? I'll be happy when we get there'.

Dad smiled and looked at them in the rear view mirror but he said nothing.

It wasn't long before they stopped.

'I'll get the tickets while you park the car', said Mum, opening her door.

'Tickets to what?' asked Daniel, looking around. All he could see was the back of a very big building in the middle of nowhere.

Dad parked and they got out and walked round to the front of the building. The two children stopped and stared. Outside the entrance was the gigantic skeleton of a Tyrannosaurus Rex.

'Wow!' said Melanie. 'It's a Dinosaur Museum!'

It was indeed. There were many kinds of dinosaur skeletons and lots of life-size models made to look as if they were in their natural surroundings. It was really awesome.

When they'd seen everything, they went into the shop and spent some of their holiday money on a 3-D jigsaw and a book.

That night, they stayed in another Bed and Breakfast and discovered that they weren't far from the coast so it was decided that the next day should be a rest day on the beach.

'Let's look for dinosaur bones', said Melanie, after they'd been in the sea.

The following day they drove for a long time.

'When are we going to get there?' asked Daniel. 'It's taking a long time to get to our holiday'.

Melanie nodded. She'd been really looking forward to the summer holiday. One year they'd been to Spain, by air, and stayed in a villa by the beach. Another time they'd gone walking in the Welsh mountains and then spent a day in Blackpool. But this year they were taking such a long time to get there.

'Let's stop at this shop', exclaimed Mum, suddenly. 'I want to buy some things for a picnic'. She grabbed her purse and disappeared into the small supermarket.

'Where are we going to eat it?' asked Melanie, looking around. 'We're in the middle of a town'.

Half an hour later, Mum had spread a cloth on the grass, under a tree, and Dad was unpacking the food.

'After lunch, we'll go and look at the animals', said Dad. 'They have deer and wild ponies and all sorts of things. I believe there is a display of birds of prey this afternoon, too, and plenty of small animals you can pet'.

Melanie and Daniel finished their picnic and helped gather everything up and bundle it into the car. Animals were their passion.

'Enjoyed yourselves today?' asked Mum, that night, and they both nodded, sleepily.

'Will we get there tomorrow?' asked Daniel, but Mum just smiled.

Late the next afternoon, the children got the biggest surprise of all. They arrived back at home!

'But . . . ', said Melanie. She was speechless.

'Why aren't we going on holiday?' asked Daniel.

'We've been on holiday', said Dad, as they pulled up in front of the garage and Mum rummaged in her bag for the keys. 'Didn't you enjoy it? You visited your cousins, went to the Water Park, the Dinosaur Museum and the beach, and then the Wildlife Park yesterday'.

'I know', said Melanie, 'but we didn't actually arrive anywhere'.

'A holiday isn't always somewhere you arrive at', said Mum, 'it's things you do along the journey. We thought what we did would make you happy' .

'Oh, it did', they both said. 'It was a great holiday!'

End

Questions

1. Who would like to tell us about a time when you were looking forward to a holiday? (take two or three, briefly).

2. *(To those who replied).*
   Can you remember what it was you were looking forward to?

3. What do you think Melanie and Daniel were looking forward to?

4. Sometimes we can spend so much time thinking about something in the future that we forget about enjoying what is happening in the present moment. Can anyone think of a time this has happened to them? (*Take examples. If none are forthcoming, give one of your own*).

5. When is the only time it is possible to be happy? (*In the present. Discuss this difficult notion with the children*).

6. Challenge the children to watch, during the week, for times they realise they are happy - can they see what the cause was?

Thought for the Day:

Sometimes we can be like Melanie and David and think that we can only be happy at some time in the future when something special happens. We can all be happy today and everyday if we choose to - we don't have to wait for special times.

Ella goes on a magical exploration to all parts of the world, but will she find what she is looking for . . . ?

The Butterfly

Ella had once been happy but now she sat, her knees under her chin and her head in her hands, crying.

'What's the matter?' said a voice.

She looked up to see a small, green man standing there. There was genuine concern in his three eyes.

Ella wiped away the tears with the back of her hand and tried to smile. 'Are you an alien?' she asked.

The little man smiled, too. 'Do I look like a human?'

She shook her head.

'Why were you weeping? Have you lost something?'

Ella nodded. 'Happiness', she said. 'I had it once but now it's gone and I don't know where to find it'.

'What does it look like?' asked the alien. 'How big is it? What colour is it? If you give me an idea I could try to help'.

Ella thought for a moment. 'I've never actually seen it', she said. 'But I know I had it once and now I've lost it. It must be invisible, I suppose'.

The alien sighed with impatience. 'Do other people have it?'

'Some do', replied Ella.

'Then ask them where they got it', said the little, green man. 'It's as simple as that'.

'You're no help', said Ella. 'I'll have to look for it myself. It must be in a difficult place to find'.

'I didn't see any sign of it when I landed just now', said the man. 'It's not in the sky. Maybe you should try looking in the sea'.

A brightly coloured butterfly hovered about Ella's face but she jumped to her feet, frightening it away.

'Good idea', she said. 'I'll go and look in the sea'.

She searched the ocean from one side to the other. She looked in underwater caves and dived among the brilliant fish and orange anemones on the coral reefs. She rode on the backs of dolphins and explored sunken wrecks, but nowhere could she find happiness.

At last, Ella climbed ashore and flopped onto the sand. The alien stood there beside his spaceship and looked at her expectantly.

'Did you find it?' he asked, but she shook her head.

'No sign of it'.

'Is it a sort of treasure?' asked the alien.

'I suppose it is'.

'Perhaps it's in the old castle over there', suggested the alien.

A coloured butterfly hung in the air just above her head but Ella jumped up.

'I'll go and see', she said.

She ran to the old castle and went in through its huge gate. She looked in the dungeons first as that seemed the most obvious place to keep treasure. They were dark and damp and empty. Then she ran around the battlements and up the spiral stone stairs into the tower. Through the turrets she looked down into the grassy courtyard where children were laughing and playing. There was happiness!

Church bells began to ring and Ella looked down and saw a bride and groom emerging from a church. There was happiness! It was here, all around her. She stood for a moment, watching, as people threw handfuls of coloured confetti over the couple. From the corner of her eye she saw another splash of colour, hovering just above her shoulder. As she turned and ran for the stairs, the butterfly was blown over the castle wall, where it landed on the bride's head among the confetti.

Ella arrived, panting, in the courtyard but the children had gone. Only the little, green man stood there, his three eyes looking at her.

'I nearly found it!' exclaimed Ella. 'At least, I saw some people who had it'.

The alien sat down on the grass and put his head in his hands to think.

'Maybe, it is guarded by a fierce animal', he said, at last. 'Can you think where that could be?'

'The jungle!' Ella said. 'That's full of fierce animals'.

So, off she went and searched through all the biggest and darkest jungles. She risked her life creeping into the dens of lions and the nests of snakes and the river homes of crocodiles, but all to no avail.

Exhausted, she arrived home again and sat on a grassy bank, by a stream, and closed her eyes.

'No luck?' asked a voice.

'No', said Ella.

'Well, I tried', said the alien. 'I'm off home, now. Good luck in your search'.

He climbed into his spaceship and Ella heard the whirring of the motor as he zoomed up into the sky.

'I'm not searching any more', said Ella, to herself. 'I'm too tired'.

She lay back and closed her eyes in the cool shade of a tree. A pretty, coloured butterfly hovered about for a moment or two before landing on her hand. Ella was too tired to move but she did open her eyes to see what it was.

The butterfly stood, its delicate wings gently moving, and Ella gazed at it in awe.

Then she looked beyond it to the stream, sparkling in the sunshine, and she listened to the birds above her in the trees. She took a deep breath and smelt the soft perfume of the flowers and a smile spread across her face.

She felt really happy.

End

Questions

1. What kinds of things make you happy? Who would like to share some things with us?

2. Ella was looking for happiness. Can you remember where she looked for it? *(The sea, an old castle, the jungle)*.

3. What was wrong with the way Ella looked for happiness? *(As if it was an object. This is difficult and may need some 'scaffolding' i.e. clues to assist thinking if necessary)*.

4. If happiness is not an 'object', what kind of thing is it?

5. Who can describe what Ella learned about happiness?

Thought for the Day:

Ella looked for happiness, everywhere, thinking it was something outside that she had to find. She finally found it was something inside of her, which was there all the time. Remember, that if happiness is inside you, you can choose to be happy any time you wish.

This modern fairy story for younger children, shows that there are subtle aspects to happiness, and that the absence of it affects everyone and everything around. Benton the Giant takes a while to learn that happiness is best!

The Magic of Happiness

You've all heard stories about giants before, haven't you? Greedy giants, like the one in 'Jack and the Beanstalk'. Stupid giants, cruel and treacherous giants, even kind giants.

This is the story of a sad and miserable giant. His name was Benton and he lived in a big house with a very large garden.

One thing that Benton liked was flowers. He loved to look at the delicate structure of their petals and stamens and marvel at their brilliant colours. He would bend and put his enormous nose near them and smell their scent. Sometimes he would just sit and watch the bees gathering nectar or the butterflies hovering about. The only trouble was, even in his vast garden, not a single flower would grow. He could only admire flowers in other people's gardens.

All the people of the village were used to Benton, of course. Some of them felt sorry for him but others thought him mean and unfriendly. He was always straying into their gardens to admire the flowers but if anyone came near his house, he would send them away with a roar and a wave of a huge fist.

Benton tried planting seeds. He watered them well and they came up, but as soon as he bent over to peer at them, they wilted, and Benton's face would droop too. He tried buying plants from the garden centre but as soon as he planted them in his own garden, they wilted and died. Once, he even paid a gardener to plant out his garden, but it was no use. The minute that Benton came out to look at the flowers, the colourful blooms bent their heads and the leaves curled up and withered. Even weeds and grass wouldn't grow, so that the giant's garden looked like a desert of dry earth and stones.

The only living thing in Benton's garden was a huge oak tree. It was hundreds of years old and far more powerful than the giant. In fact, sometimes when the giant sat under its gnarled branches on hot summer days, even he looked small by comparison.

Children sometimes looked into his garden as it seemed like a good place to kick a ball around and the oak tree looked inviting to climb. But Benton the giant would roar and shake his massive fist and they would run back home, holding their hands over their ears.

One day, he was sick. When he awoke in the morning he felt very hot and shivery. He tried to get out of bed but almost fell over as dizziness overcame him.

'Oooh, I feel bad', he moaned, and lay down in bed again.

For three days he stayed there, just managing, sometimes, to get a drink of water or go to the bathroom. No-one knew he was ill. No-one came to visit him or make him something nice to eat. He had no friends at all and didn't even have a phone because there was no-one to ring him.

On the fourth day, he felt a little better and sat up on the side of the bed. Something caught his eye outside the window and he stood up for a better look. There were children playing in a corner of his garden!

Benton leapt to his feet, raising his fist and preparing to bang on the window and bellow to frighten them away.

But his legs felt weak and could hardly hold him and his arms felt heavy and flopped back to his side. Even the bellow in his throat came out as a whisper.
Benton slumped back on the bed, annoyed. He would get them! When he was better he would teach them a lesson.

It took several more days for the giant to recover completely and all the time he could hear the laughter and shouts of the children having fun in his garden. He did not look out of his window because he knew it would make him so cross to see them that he was likely to smash the window in his rage.

At last, he felt better and early one morning he went downstairs. He opened the front door, quietly, and peered out.

'Good', he said to himself. 'The children haven't arrived yet, but when they do, they are in for a big fright'.

Benton crept outside and hid behind the big, oak tree. Then he waited. Soon, the children arrived, skipping and laughing. The giant watched as they entered his gate and went over to the corner where they had been playing. Then he took a deep breath.

'AAAAAAGGHH!' he roared.

The children screamed and fled with Benton striding after them, making sure they were well away from his gate. Then he turned back towards his house.

But something caught his eye. In the corner, where the children had been playing, a thick, carpet of grass covered the ground. Through it daisies and buttercups poked their heads. Around the edges were clumps of forget-me-nots, lupins and foxgloves and many other wild flowers.

Benton couldn't believe his eyes! He strode over for a closer look but as he reached them the colours faded, the flower petals fell and the grass turned brown. Before his eyes the garden disappeared leaving only brown, dusty earth.

What had made the garden grow? What magic did the children possess?

He remembered the sound of their happy voices and laughter, their shrieks and giggles and shouts as they played. Was that what it was?

Benton ran back towards the gate and along the road.

'Come back!' he shouted. 'Children! Come Back!'

The children stopped running and turned around, unable to believe their ears. There stood Benton waving his hand to bring them back instead of his fist to shoo them away.

Slowly, they went back. What had made the giant change? They were suspicious at first.

'Why are you calling us back?' asked one brave boy.

'Because you have the magic of happiness', said the giant. 'You made my garden bloom. Come in and see for yourselves'.

The children trooped in and soon forgot the giant and started to play again. Benton watched from his doorway.

Little by little, spikes of green grass sprouted and thickened into a lawn. Flowers opened their petals in a rainbow of colours. Soon, bees and dragonflies arrived, and birds sang from the oak tree. A butterfly swayed gently on a lupin.

As the children ran around the garden, so it grew and bloomed and became alive and the giant smiled and then he threw back his head and laughed. And what a wonderful feeling that was.

From then on, people came from miles around to visit the giant's wonderful garden. They sat and had picnics on the lawn and he dug a lake so that they could enjoy the water, too. A flock of swans made it their home.

Benton was the happiest giant in the world.

End

Questions

1. Benton didn't like children, and he was always feeling miserable, but what was the one thing that he did like?

2. Do you think this shows us anything about Benton?

3. Why did Benton call the children back after he had been shouting at them?

4. Have you ever been unhappy and seen what effect it has on others? *(Hear examples from the children)*. What effect does being happy have on other people? *(Hear more examples)*.

5. Why do you think this happens? *(That others are affected by our state?)*

Thought for the Day:

You can have an effect on other people just by the way you feel. If you feel happy you can make others happy, just like the children did to Benton. If you are miserable – you will make others miserable – it is up to you!

Goodness

Goodness is literally the quality or condition of being good. This leads one to ask, 'So, therefore, what is good?' Does good depend on one's point of view? Does that point of view set up conflicts in the mind about notions of good and bad? Do good things appear bad to the person who leads a corrupt life? Even if these things are true, 'good' is accepted as meaning morally excellent of conduct; agreeable, useful and reliable.

Good is made all the better for being plentiful. It is, in fact, what we are naturally. It is possible for individuals to move towards this by examining the meaning of good, through good company *(by which is meant people, books, music - everything with which we surround ourselves)* and through keeping what is learned 'in the heart'.

These stories explore various notions of goodness, and give examples of the lives of others that can be examined and discussed. The idea of example in the learning of the concept of goodness is extremely important.

Julie has been having a hard time with her brother, who seemed to take great delight in annoying her. Through learning to give care and attention to a plant, and seeing the results, Julie came to see that there was another way of living with her brother.

The Girl Who Didn't Love

Julie arrived at school with a big scowl on her face, and it stayed there all day. She snapped at any of her classmates who spoke to her and answered very curtly anything her teacher, Mr Townville, asked.

When it was home time, Mr Townville called her over.

'I wondered what the matter was, Julie', he said. 'You don't look very happy today'.

Julie shook her head, vigorously.

'Has someone upset you?' Mr Townville sat on the corner of his desk.

'It's my brother', said Julie.

'Edward?' asked the teacher.

Julie nodded. 'I hate him'.

'That's a very strong word', said Mr Townville, shaking his head with disbelief.
'I'm sure you don't mean that'.

'I do!' said Julie. 'I hate him! He's a pest. He's horrible. I wish he didn't come to the same school as me! I wish I didn't have a brother at all!'

Mr Townville pulled out his chair. 'Sit down here, Julie, and tell me what he's done to make you feel like this'.

'He laughs and calls me names', Julie said. 'He laughs and makes fun of me and all his silly little friends in Reception copy him. It's really embarrassing'.

Mr Townville nodded. He knew that Julie's brother had started school the previous autumn.

'Not only that', went on Julie. 'The really worst thing he did was to get felt pen on my new top! And he did it on purpose, I know he did. I could tell by the way he laughed when I told Mum. He did it on purpose, and I was going to wear that top to the End-of-Term Disco on Saturday. It was new and really cool and no-one else has got one like it'.

Julie's scowl had lifted a little as she left school. Mr Townville had listened to her, and that helped, but she still hated Edward!

Friday was the last day of school before the summer holidays and everyone was in high spirits. Not much work was done that day, either. At home time, Mr Townville again called Julie over and when everyone had gone he walked over to the window sill.

'I wondered if you would do something for me over the holidays, Julie?' he said, picking up a plant pot.

'This poor plant needs some care and attention. Would you look after it during the holidays, please?'

Julie looked at the plant. Its leaves were all withered and dry and the stalks drooped. There were no flowers, and never had been as far as she could remember, although she wasn't at all interested in plants. Then she eyed the others on the window sill. If she had to look after one, why couldn't it be one of those? At least they looked alive.

But she just nodded and said nothing. She took the plant and walked out of the classroom.

On the way home, in the bus, she felt silly holding it and put it on the floor where it got kicked and knocked over but, when she picked it up, she saw that the soil was so hard and dry that none had spilled out.

At home, she watered the plant, placed it on her window sill, and almost forgot about it. A few days later, she noticed that one of the withered leaves had fallen off and she pulled at one or two more. Underneath, to her surprise, was a little green shoot! So, the plant was not dead after all!

Day by day, Julie took more interest as the tiny shoots became curled up leaves which grew and unfurled. She remembered to water it every week and even repotted it with new compost which she found in the garden shed.

Then, one morning, she noticed something else. A bud!

What would the flower be like, she wondered. What colour would it be? On the first day of the new term she carried the plant proudly in the bus and then into the classroom and put it on Mr Townville's desk. She couldn't wait to see the look on his face when he saw it!

The teacher smiled when he saw the lovely, green plant with its orange flowers. He glanced across at Julie and then carried the plant to the window sill where it had been before.

'You must have green fingers, Julie', he said. The class laughed but Julie didn't mind.

Later, during break, Mr Townville called her over again.

'Well done', he said, smiling. 'You've done wonders with that plant. See what a little love and attention can do? It can work miracles'.

Julie nodded, pleased with herself. 'I really hated it at first', she said. 'It seemed a waste of time'.

'Do you remember what you said about your brother, Edward, last term?' he asked.

'I said I hated him too', said Julie.

'Well', said Mr Townville. 'The same remedy will work for him. A little love and attention. Why don't you try it and see?

End

Questions

1. Who can sum up how Julie felt about her brother at the beginning of the story?

2. How did Julie feel about being given the plant by Mr Townville?

3. What made her begin to feel differently about the plant?

4. How exactly did she feel towards it?

5. What did Julie give to the plant, and what did she receive?

6. Mr Townville told Julie she should give her brother Edward a little love and attention. What could Julie actually do? What are examples of things she could actually do?

7. What might her brother gain? What could she gain?

Thought for the Day:

A wise person once said, 'Give what you think you lack'. Julie thought she lacked peace and friendship with her brother so she had to give it first.

This story is set in the depression of the 1930's. It shows the compassion of two boys towards a classmate, and the practical efforts they make to help him. It also shows the importance of doing good without making a big show of it.

The Boy With No Shoes

'Only a week to go!' said Alan, opening the lid of his desk and taking out his pencils. 'Then no school for six weeks. Yippee!' He slammed the lid down, just as Mr Marshall, the teacher, walked in.

'My Dad's getting us a wireless!' hissed his friend, Derek, from across the aisle. 'Off someone who's out of work. You can come round and listen to it'.

'Quiet!' Mr Marshall rapped his desk with his cane. 'Please take out your maths books. Who hasn't done their homework?'

Derek grinned at Alan under cover of his desk lid. It would be smashing to have a wireless. They'd be able to listen to 'Children's Hour' with Uncle Mac and music and . . .

'Derek Ross!' said Mr Marshall. 'Instead of skulking under your desk, perhaps you would collect up the homework books, please'.

'Yes, sir', said Derek, scraping his chair back and getting to his feet.

'And when you've done that, please fill up the ink wells ready for penmanship'.

Just before the bell went, for playtime, Mr Marshall reminded the class about the end of term 'Achievement Presentation' which took place every year. Pupils showed what they had learned during the year by reciting poetry, saying tables or reading essays they had written. Sometimes the boys showed and explained things they had made during woodwork or metalwork and the girls did the same with their needlework and cookery.

The Presentation was held in the evening so that parents could attend.

Derek and Alan sat in the playground, leaning against the wall of the school, discussing what they were going to do. Alan, being a practical sort of boy, was going to talk about the bread board he had made, with the design carved around the edge. Derek, who fancied himself as an actor and loved an audience, was going to recite 'The Charge of the Light Brigade'.

'Hey, Maurice!' Alan called to a boy, nearby. 'What are you going to do for the Presentation?'

The boy shrugged and came over and flopped down beside them. He was small and thin and his feet were bare. As he sat, cross-legged, Alan could see that the soles of his feet were thickly callused from going without shoes.

'Times tables, probably', he said, picking a bit of hard skin off a big toe. 'I'm good at those'.

After school, as Derek and Alan walked home, they remembered Maurice's bare feet.

'His Dad's been out of work for years', said Derek, 'and he's gone on one of those hunger marches to London'.

Alan nodded. 'Out of all their kids, only Jack's got shoes because he's the eldest. But I was thinking - what about the Presentation? It's going to be awful for Maurice on stage without shoes in front of all the parents'.

As the week went on, the two boys thought more and more about Maurice's lack of shoes. It was 1933 and the height of the depression and most of them only had one pair of shoes. Often they were second hand or hand-me-downs, but no-one else in their class had none at all.

'We can't lend him ours', said Derek. 'And I've got all sisters. What about your brother, Joe? Could you borrow a pair of his?'

'They'd be much too big', said Alan. 'He takes sevens and you know how small Maurice's feet are. He'd fall out of them - that's if Joe would lend them in the first place'.

There seemed to be no answer to the problem. It was no use asking anyone else in the class. No-one was that well off that they had spare shoes. Some might have wellingtons, but that was no good.

It was on the morning of the Presentation that Alan had an idea.

'We take off our shoes, too', he said, beaming.

Derek looked at him, in surprise.

'If we can't get any shoes for Maurice', explained Alan, 'we'll go barefoot, too. Then he won't be the only one!'

28

Derek slapped him on the back. 'That's a smashing idea! We'll do it. But don't tell Maurice'.

That evening, the parents and families trooped into the School Hall and took their seats.

Alan could see his own mum and dad in the second row. His mum had put on her best hat and was sitting with her hands folded in her lap, looking expectantly at the stage. They were going to be surprised to see him in bare feet.

The children went on stage in groups and then each did their own presentation. Maurice was in the group in front of Alan and Derek and, in fact, it was so crowded back stage that they didn't see him go on.

'Next group get ready', said Mr Marshall, standing in the wings. There was the applause from the audience and the clump of feet as the previous group trouped off the stage. There was Maurice amongst them.

But Alan and Derek stared. He was wearing shoes!

They both looked down at their own bare feet. It was too late to do anything now. They were on!

Alan noticed his parents' look of surprise as he stood, barefoot, explaining about his bread board and it almost distracted him.

When their group had finished and marched off they sought out Maurice.

'Where did you get the shoes?' they asked.

Maurice grinned. 'Off Mr Marshall. His son got a new pair so he gave me his old ones. Smart, aren't they? It feels funny wearing them'.

Alan and Derek laughed and went to get their own shoes and put them on.

End

Questions

1. Think about when the story took place and see how many pieces of evidence you can find for your answer. *(Ask who has one piece of evidence, two . . . three . . . etc. Ask children for their evidence).*

2. Why would Alan and Derek bother about Maurice, when they already had shoes?

3. What makes people do things for others? *(Take a range of reasons, including the not so altruistic ones! How many ways can each child think of?)*

4. Can anyone remember a time when you did something for somebody? *(Take two or three).*

5. *(Directing to those who answered).*
   What made you do it? How did you feel? Think about the large scale. What would school *(life)* be like if nobody helped anyone else, and what would it be like if everyone helped each other? *(Leave that question for children to consider, and perhaps for further discussion in class).*

Thought for the Day:

There are two parts to doing good to someone. The first is doing the action, the second is doing it without a big fuss or wanting to be noticed for doing it. Try to see an opportunity to do something for someone without telling everyone how good you are.

This story reflects the meaning of goodness through the example of Mother Theresa and her work with the destitute in Calcutta. Children are encouraged to not only admire the example, but to consider why anyone might choose such a life.

A Pencil in the Hand of God

The train rattled through the countryside leaving a long billow of smoke behind it. As it approached a village it whistled, shrilly.

In a corner of one of the crowded carriages a small person was awoken by the whistle. She sat up and adjusted her veil, for she was a nun. Then she looked out of the window to watch the landscape go by. A landscape which had once been alien to her but now was commonplace, for she had lived here, in India, for seventeen years now, teaching at a Roman Catholic High School for girls in Calcutta. She loved her work there but had recently been ill and was travelling to Darjeeling for a rest in a religious retreat.

The small nun was called Sister Theresa although that was not her real name. She had been born Agnes Gonxha Bojaxhui in 1910 in Skopje, which is now in Serbia.

It was 1946 and she was thirty six years old and had never been back to her homeland.

As she sat, staring out of the window, she heard someone speak and turned, politely, to see who it was. There were people all around, sitting, crammed on the seats, standing in the aisle, but none were looking at her. Who had spoken?

Sister Theresa shrugged and turned back to the window.

The voice spoke again, and this time she realised, with awe, that clear as it was, it was not a human voice. It was inside her head, yet real at the same time. She had heard this voice before when she was twelve years old, back in Skopje.

It was the voice who had told her of her destiny to serve God.

'Leave your teaching at the convent', said the voice. 'You have much greater work to do'.

Sister Theresa listened, with some disappointment. She loved her work and didn't want to leave. It would be a very difficult thing to do.

'You must serve me amongst the poorest of the poor', said the voice.

Two years later, Sister Theresa left the convent with a dozen other nuns and started her 'Little Society'. The nuns would walk the darkest, dirtiest streets of Calcutta seeking out the poorest and sickest people to help. They had to learn to beg for their own meals and had to suffer a lot of abuse and humiliation.

In 1952, Mother Theresa, as she was now called, opened the Nirmal Hrday *(Pure Heart)* Home for Dying Destitutes of Calcutta, where people who were dying, in terribly inhuman circumstances, were brought to be cared for in peace and love for their final days. They were washed, fed and their sores treated. They were shown that, although society had cast them out, they were loved.

At first, the nuns were not welcome in a city which was largely Hindu and it took time for them to be accepted, then loved, by the people and authorities.

Mother Theresa not only served her community in Calcutta but strived for world peace and travelled all over the world wherever she was needed. She went to Ethiopia to help the hungry, at times of great famine, to care for the radiation victims of Chernobyl and the earthquake victims in Armenia.

Many awards were bestowed on her including the Nobel Peace Prize, in 1979. She accepted all these awards on behalf of the poor, using any money to fund her centres.

When praised for her work she said, 'I am like a little pencil in God's hand. He does the thinking. He does the writing. The pencil has only to be allowed to be used'.

Mother Theresa died on September 5th, 1997, at the age of 87 years. She was succeeded by Sister Nirmala who is now head of the Missionaries of Charity.

Today, over 5000 Sisters, Brothers and volunteers run 500 centres, world-wide, which operate workshops for the unemployed, food centres, orphanages and refuges for people suffering from leprosy, mental illness or old age.

Mother Theresa left a wonderful legacy which will never be forgotten.

End

Questions

1. Agnes Bojaxhui left her friends and family to become a nun in India. What kinds of things would make someone take the decision to do that?

2. Most people would find it difficult to leave their country, family and friends. What for you would be difficult about this?

3. When Mother Theresa first started her group in Calcutta, why didn't people like and accept them *(at first)*, even though they were doing good?

4. In time, most of the people who didn't like her changed their minds. Why do you think this was?

5. Mother Theresa said, 'I am like a little pencil in God's hand. He does the thinking. He does the writing. The pencil only has to be allowed to be used'. What does this mean?

6. If she had been a different kind of person, what might have stopped Mother Theresa from allowing herself to be used?

Thought for the Day:

Mother Theresa put up with terrible hardship to help others. Sometimes things become a little more difficult for ourselves if we choose to help someone else. We call that making a sacrifice. It is good to make sacrifices in looking after others.

This story not only shows goodness, but also several other qualities. Nelson Mandela never gave up hope during the dark days of his imprisonment. He emerged to become the first democratically elected President of South Africa. The example set by such a life becomes the embodiment of so many of the virtues - a life of goodness through service, which needed great patience to achieve justice leading inevitably to happiness!

The Struggle is My Life

'Here we all work on the Mississippi . . . '

The deep, warm voice of Paul Robeson began the familiar song as Nelson Mandela stepped out onto the veranda and settled himself in his chair. Although an old man, he moved with a litheness that belied his age, his strict daily exercise regime saw to that.

This was his favourite time of day. He looked out at the long shadows stretching across the landscape of his beloved homeland, Qunu, in the Transkei, and sighed with pleasure. The sun was just sinking below the horizon and the sky was streaked with red and orange. He let the wonderful voice of his favourite singer and the mood of the song seep into his being and bring memories from the past into his mind.

> *'Show me the way to the River Jordan,*
> *There's an old stream that I long to cross'.*

Slavery. When life was so terrible that the only thing they had to look forward to was the freedom of death.

The black people of South Africa had not been slaves, but neither had they had the freedom and rights of the whites. The regime had been called Apartheid, meaning that the races were kept apart and segregated.

> *'He don't plant taters, he don't plant cotton,*
> *But them that plants 'em is soon forgotten,*
> *But ol' man river, he just keeps rollin' along'.*

How the slaves must have envied that mighty river, he thought. Deep and wide and serene, and seeming oblivious to the terrible suffering which was taking place on its banks.

As a boy, Nelson had dreamed of making a contribution to the freedom struggle of his people. He had completed a Bachelor of Arts degree by correspondence at Johannesburg and commenced studying for his Law Degree. In 1942 he had joined the African National Congress.

The ANC's aim was to attain full equality for all South Africans, whatever their colour or race. That, among other things, they should have representation in Parliament and free and compulsory education for all children.

The ANC's policy was one of non-violence, their weapons being of boycott, strike, civil disobedience and non co-operation and when the Campaign for the Defiance of Unjust Laws was launched in 1952, Nelson had been elected National Volunteer-in-Chief. His role was to travel the country organising resistance to discrimination.

For his part in this, he was given a six month suspended sentence and confined to Johannesburg for six months. During this time he was admitted to the profession of attorney and opened a practice in the city but later the authorities demanded that he move it to 'the back of beyond' and a petition was also made to strike him off the Roll of Attorneys. This was unsuccessful.

At this time, Nelson became Deputy President of the ANC and during the whole of the 50's was the victim of repression and was banned, arrested and imprisoned.

> ' . . . you get a little drunk and you land in jail'.

Nelson thought of all those years in prison. Twenty-five years. The ultimate loss of freedom. Locked in a cell during the day. Deprived of his beloved music, too. He remembered the concerts that were organised from time to time, especially at Christmas, and the voices of the other prisoners as they sung carols.

The charge was one of sabotage. When he had become leader of the Umkhonto we Sizwe, the military wing of the ANC, a campaign of sabotage against government and economic installations had been launched.

'It was only when all else had failed', he had said, 'when all channels of peaceful protest had been barred to us, that the decision was made to embark on violent forms of political struggle. The government has left us no other choice'.

His statement from the dock at the end of the trial ends with these words:

'I have fought against white domination, and I have fought against black domination. I have cherished the ideal of a democratic and free society in which all persons live together in harmony and with equal opportunities. It is an ideal which I hope to live for and to achieve. But if needs be, it is an ideal for which I am prepared to die'.

Nelson Mandela was released on 11th February 1990 and immediately continued his life's work. He became President of the ANC, now legal, and later, in May 1994, he was the first democratically elected State President of South Africa and continued as such until his retirement in June 1999.

In 1993, he accepted the Nobel Peace Prize on behalf of all South Africans who had suffered and sacrificed so much to bring peace to their land.

> *'Ah gets weary and sick of tryin'*
> *'Ah'm tired of livin' an' scared of dyin',*

The sky was darkening now and a brisk breeze rustled the leaves. Nelson smiled and shook his head, slightly. He had never got sick of trying, and in the end he had achieved many of his goals. Nor was he tired of living. There was so much to enjoy - his beloved country, and music, to name two.

He got up from his chair and went back into the house. Lifting Paul Robeson from the CD machine he slipped another in and pressed PLAY.

Tchaikowsky's 'Fourth Symphony' filled the room and immediately lifted his spirits.

End

Questions

1. Nelson Mandela chose to oppose the ideas of South Africa as they were when he was young. What made him choose to do this?

2. Twenty five years is a long long time to spend in jail. What would some of the difficulties have been? What would have been some of the things that might have given him hope?

3. Nelson said he wanted, 'A free society in which all persons live together in harmony and with equal opportunities'. What does this mean? What sorts of things, *in practice*, could make this true?

4. Do you have 'Equal Opportunities' in school or home? Give reasons for your example.

5. If you have harmony in your classroom, does it stay all the time or do you have to work to keep it? *(Seek reasons and examples for answers).*

Thought for the day:

Harmony and fairness are just as important in a family, a class or a school as they are in a city or a country. See what you can do to make this school a fair and harmonious one.

This fable shows that one does not have to be strong and powerful to be good. Each individual has talents that can be used for the good of others. These acts of goodness need not be huge events, but just everyday situations that arise in each individual's life. The events will keep coming but we can choose how we deal with them!

The Lion and the Mouse
(Aesop's Fable)

A lion was out one day searching for food. He hadn't had much luck and was getting hungry. His tummy was rumbling very loudly.

Suddenly, he spotted a mouse, dashing through the grass. The lion swiped with his great paw and grabbed the mouse in his claws. It was only a small mouse but would be better than nothing.

'Oh, please, Sir', said the mouse, 'don't eat me. Great and honourable lion, King of all beasts. Please let me go. I have six children at home who will have no father if you kill me'.

The lion was flattered by all this reverence. For a moment he wavered. Then he felt the hunger pangs again and opened his mouth wide.

'I beg you', said the mouse, 'if you spare my life I will save yours one day'.

Instead of eating the mouse, the lion threw back his head and laughed. 'You, save me? That's impossible'. But he was so amused at the mouse that he did let him go and the mouse scampered back to his family.

Some weeks later, some huntsmen came into the jungle. They trapped the lion in a net and pulled it tight so that he couldn't move and then left him beside a tree. At the end of the day, they intended to come back for him. Then who knows what would happen.

Along came the little mouse, skipping and scampering. It stopped short when it saw the trapped lion. Then it ran up and began gnawing through the net. It was a big job for a little mouse but, all day long, it chewed and chewed and never once stopped for a rest. At last, the mouse chewed through the last bit of net and the lion was free. It was almost sunset and the huntsmen were due back any minute.

The lion bent his big head down to the mouse. 'Thank you little mouse', he said. 'You kept your word and saved my life, even though I thought it was impossible'.

End

Questions

1. How did the lion show goodness?

2. How did the mouse show goodness? *(Be sure that 'keeping his word' is one of the answers)*.

3. What made the lion think it would be impossible for the mouse to save his life?

4. Think of some things that you are good at - your talents. *(Take examples)*.

5. Who can remember using a talent in a way that showed goodness? *(Take examples)*.

Thought for the Day:

We can use our talents selfishly or for the good of all. We become what we practice, so if we practice doing good, we become good. Everyone is able to choose the way they want to be.

Service

The concept of Service has all but been lost, especially since the majority of people link the word with the derivation from the Latin, servitium, meaning slavery. It doesn't help that youngsters are brought up in a society which stresses individual rights, with little thought for responsibility. More appropriate to the theme in this book is the quotation from the Book of Common Prayer, which says 'God . . . whose service is perfect freedom'. This carries with it the sense of an action of 'serving, helping, or benefiting; conduct tending to the welfare or advantage of another' as described in The Shorter Oxford English Dictionary. This is the premise upon which the stories have been written - that it is important to move out beyond seeing to one's own needs to considering the needs of others. Implicit in this is the notion that in breaking out from the constraints of a 'small world' the individual does indeed move towards freedom. This, however, has to be thoroughly discussed so that children can have the opportunity to test it in practice - philosophy is little use if not practical!

Patrick is good at looking after himself, and also at looking after his pet birds. He accidentally discovers what it is like to do something for someone else, and finds it is just the same as looking after his birds.

The Thrush

'Patrick, would you do Brown's Farm for me today? I've still got some homework to do'.

Patrick shook his head, humping his newspaper bag onto his bike. 'I've got my birds to feed, Mike. Your homework's your problem'.

'I should have known better than to ask you', muttered Mike, as he rode off.

In a moment, Patrick had forgotten about Mike as he pedalled swiftly towards his paper round area. Later, when he got home, he went out the back to his small aviary of budgies. Twelve he had now, all colours, and one pair was nesting.

'Breakfast time!' he called as he opened the wire mesh door and went in with a box of food in his hand. He smiled as several of the birds landed on his head and shoulders.

Soon, they were fed and cleaned and Patrick changed for school.

'See you, Mum', he called, opening the front door.

'Oh, Patrick, call in and get my dry-cleaning on the way home from school, please', said his mum. But Patrick had shut the door and was on his bike again. Straight after school, he was going round to his best mate, Ben's, house to hear his new CD and he'd feel a real wally taking Mum's dry-cleaning with him.

Anyway, he thought, didn't she always say people should be independent and try to help themselves? Well, he agreed. He didn't help anyone and he never asked for help either. Most people knew better than to ask him.

That evening, when he went to see his birds, he almost tripped over one on the path. It wasn't a budgie, but a wild bird, a thrush, he thought. He almost left it. It looked nearly dead, anyway. Some cat must have got it. He almost pushed it off the path with his foot.

43

But, what if it had been one of his budgies?

Gently, he picked up the bird and it chirped, weakly. He took it indoors and found a small box which he lined with a couple of his mum's soft dusters. Then he laid the bird in it and took it up to his bedroom.

Several times during the night he woke up and looked at the bird. It was still alive and as dawn broke it began to chirp. The thrush sang and sang, its voice sweet and tuneful.

But, the next time Patrick looked, it was dead.

He felt a sudden sadness. How could it sing so beautifully when it was so near to death? He envied the bird its happiness.

During his paper round he thought of nothing but the bird.

As he was feeding his budgies, later on, he heard a faint sound from the garden, next door. It was a weak, moaning sound. An old lady lived there, Mrs Parker. The sound came again and, out of curiosity, Patrick climbed on the dustbin and looked over the fence.

She lay there in a crumpled heap, just by her back door. What was she doing? Why didn't she get up? Patrick jumped off the bin. Old people were really funny. Anyway, he didn't have time. He finished cleaning out the aviary and went indoors.

He thought of the bird again. How sad it had looked. It must have been in pain yet it sang so beautifully on that last dawn of its life. He'd tell his mum about Mrs Parker.

But for some reason he went himself. As he opened her side gate he could hear her weak calls again.

She was pale and shaking but her eyes were open.

'Patrick', she said, weakly. 'Please get help. I've been out here all night and I think I've broken my leg'.

Patrick sped back home and phoned for an ambulance. Then he took a blanket and covered the old lady up. The ambulance soon arrived, siren wailing, and the paramedics carefully put Mrs Parker onto the stretcher and loaded her into the ambulance. As they passed him, Mrs Parker held out a hand and gripped Patrick's.

'God bless you, dear', she whispered.

44

It was just like the thrush singing, thought Patrick.

He thought about Mrs Parker over the next few days and hoped that she hadn't died, like the bird had. It seemed silly to think so much about someone he hardly knew and she was old.

One day, when he got home from school, he decided that there was something he had to do before he went to look at his birds.

He phoned the hospital and asked about Mrs Parker.

She was all right! She'd had a pin put in her broken leg and she would be home soon.

Patrick smiled, in fact, he almost felt like laughing out aloud. He felt, suddenly, very happy.

On the day Mrs Parker was expected home he finished his paper round and then went round to the florist and bought a big bunch of flowers.

End

Questions

1. Take a couple of minutes to consider what this story is really about.

2. Why didn't people usually ask Patrick for help?

3. What made Patrick care for the bird?

4. How could a person speaking be considered to be like a bird singing?

5. What is it that makes most people like birds singing?

6. What does it feel like to care for, or do things for, other people? Has anyone any examples?

7. What happens when you do things for other people? *(Look for several different responses).*

8. If you do things for other people, does it mean you stop doing things for yourself?

Thought for the Day:

Try to observe how many times in a day you do something for someone else. It doesn't have to be something big, such as Patrick getting help for Mrs Parker, it can be simply seeing that someone needed help in something, and you helped. See how you feel at the time, and see how the other person feels.

Thousands of pigeons were used in both World Wars to carry messages and some even had tiny cameras strapped to their chests. Many lives were saved by the Pigeon Corps and many brave birds were awarded medals.

Poppy, the War Pigeon

'It's time to go to work, Poppy', said the soldier. He reached into the pigeon's cage and gently lifted out the bird.

'We're surrounded by the enemy', he said. 'You must fly home and get help'.

Poppy could hear the thump of heavy guns all around, making the ground shake. Thick, black smoke made it difficult to breathe. She knew that, once again, she had an important job to do.

The soldier attached a little capsule to her leg. Inside it was a message.

'Good luck, Poppy', said the other soldiers. They looked tired and grey as they sat, leaning against the sand bag wall of the trench. Some were wounded and lay covered with grey blankets.

Everything was grey, Poppy thought.

The soldier stroked her soft head with one finger. 'You are our last hope', he whispered. Then he opened his hand and released her into the sky.

Poppy soared upwards. The crack of gunfire and noise of exploding shells made her small body shudder. Through dense black smoke she flew, over the enemy soldiers and away towards home.

Long ago, before the war started, she had flown over this countryside. Then, there were golden fields of wheat and lush, green grass with cattle grazing. There were villages with laughing children playing and birds singing in the trees.

Now, it was grey and black. The fields had turned to mud and the trees to burnt black stumps as the armies swept over them.

A wind began to blow and heavy clouds blotted out the sun. Spears of jagged, orange lightning flashed and thunder cracked. Then the rain started.

Soon, Poppy's body felt heavy as her feathers became wet and she struggled to fly against the pounding rain. Water streamed over her eyes so that she could hardly see. Which way was home? She must get back, quickly. It was very important. But, if the wind blew her off course she might get lost. She might be caught by enemy soldiers who would read the message hidden in the little capsule fixed to her leg.

Poppy was tired. She was so tired that she just wanted to fly down and find shelter and warmth somewhere. And some grain to eat.

Then the rain stopped and the sky cleared a little. Now she could see some buildings ahead. A village, and a church with a tower. She would just rest for a minute.

She landed on the edge of the tower and clung to the bricks, water dripping off her wings. She looked around, unsure of which way to go.

There was no sound in the village. No people or dogs or cats. No children playing. Many of the houses were just heaps of rubble. And, Poppy was lost. She thought of the soldiers trapped by the enemy. Young men who might die if they weren't rescued. So she spread her wings and took off, heading south, and hoping it was the right way.

Suddenly, a man jumped out of the shadows. He had seen Poppy and he put his rifle to his shoulder and fired.

Poppy felt an awful pain in her leg and she dropped down towards the earth. She mustn't be caught. Her leg was injured but she could still fly. It was the leg with the message capsule attached. With all her strength she soared into the sky again.

The sun came out and warmed her cold, wet body until her feathers felt light and fluffy again. Now, when she looked down she could see red. Fields and fields of red. The whole world seemed to be covered in a huge, red carpet. But it wasn't the red blood of the poor soldiers killed or wounded in the Great War. It was poppies. Hundreds and thousands of poppies, bright red, dancing in the sun, waving their bright faces towards the sky.

Keep going, they seemed to say to Poppy. Keep going and take your important message home so that the soldiers will be saved. And Poppy flew on despite the pain in her leg. She knew where she was now. She knew these trees and these buildings. She knew this pigeon loft.

She knew the man who stood, waiting, his face turned towards the sky.

'Poppy!' said the man, holding out his arm. Poppy flew down onto her owner's arm, cooing softly, her injured leg hanging.

The man's face crumpled when he saw Poppy's leg. 'Oh, my poor bird', he said. 'You've been shot'.

But the message capsule was still there and he gently took it off. Then he put Poppy into the coop and laid her on a bed of soft straw near some grain and water.

'You'll be all right', said the man. 'You're a very brave bird but your war service is over, now that you have only one good leg. This was your forty-fifth mission but it was your last'.

Poppy saw the man smile and again felt a soft hand stroke her feathers. Then she snuggled down into the straw and went to sleep.

Poppy seeds can lay in the earth a long time and only begin to grow when the soil is turned over. During the First World War so much of the soil was turned over by the soldiers, horses, vehicles and exploding shells that poppies grew and bloomed as they never had before.

End

Questions

1. Service is to do with seeing to the needs of others. Can anyone give personal examples of this?

2. Can you think of any reasons why people do things for others, that is, see to their needs?

3. What are reasons we sometimes give for not doing these things?

4. Has anyone any examples of animals seeing to the needs of other animals? For what reasons do they do these things?

5. What about animals seeing to the needs of humans? *(Guide dogs, animals in hospitals, canaries in mines).*
   Why do they do these things? *(There are a variety of reasons).*

6. How do you feel when you look after someone else?

Thought for the Day:

The world seems to be a better place when we all look after each other. We shouldn't exclude animals from this - we should look after them carefully, and sometimes they look after us. All creatures are connected in the unity of the creation.

Stephen was not at all looking forward to his visit to Cranfield House old folks' home. What would he say to the residents? Couldn't his time be better spent? Stephen finds that experience of something is not always like the idea we have of it.

Old Memories

Stephen didn't like PSD. Well, it wasn't that he didn't like it but he was shy and it often entailed talking to people, which he knew he was no good at.

The current project was visiting a home for elderly people. Stephen didn't know any old people and hadn't a clue what he would talk about. Anyway, some of them were a bit daft, weren't they? Talked nonsense. It would be really boring. Every Friday afternoon, for four weeks, they would spend an hour at Cranfield House.

He wasn't the only one who was dreading this project either. No-one wanted to do it. And Miss Medway was going to be choosing the first six this morning. Well, he might as well get it over with and volunteer for the first group.

His heart was thumping as they went in. The lady in charge took them towards a small sitting room.

'Here are some children from Beckfield Primary to talk to you', she said, to the five old people sitting there, who were looking at them with interest.

Then, she turned to the children. 'Two of you can come in here. This is George, Dolly, Betty, Bill and Margaret'.

Stephen stepped forward and so did Julie. Now, what should they do? A whole hour!

'Come in! Sit down!' said the one called George, smiling. 'It's kind of you to visit. It'll be real nice to talk to some young people'.

Stephen had made a small list of questions to ask but he thought it would be rude to fish it out of his pocket now. He racked his brains to think of what he'd written but George was already asking him about school and where he lived.

'You live in the end house in Pears Road? My, I remember the people who lived there when I was a lad. A funny lot they were. Used to keep goats and let them in the house like pets! I could tell you a story or two about them!' And he did.

The hour went very quickly and by the end of it Stephen had only spoken to George and Betty. He'd found himself telling them about school and his hobbies. When he mentioned building model aircraft, Betty had asked him to bring one next time to show her. Why would an old lady want to see a plane?

He found out the following week.

Betty took the model and looked at it closely. Then she smiled up at him.

'During the war I helped to build aircraft', she said. 'Not ones like this of course, this is modern'.

'What sort did you build?' asked Stephen.

'We never knew', said Betty. 'It was secret, you see. Best that we didn't know. My husband was away fighting in the War so we women helped by working in the factories. Dolly here used to fly bombers all over Britain delivering them to air bases where they were needed, didn't you, Dolly?' The lady next to Betty nodded her head.

'Wow!' said Stephen, incredulously. It was amazing.

Then he chatted with Bill who was interested in computers and who listened intently as Stephen explained all about the Internet. He had to talk fairly loudly to Bill as he couldn't hear very well and kept fiddling with his hearing aid.

At one point, one of the carers came in and announced that it was Bill's bath day. Bill pulled a face.

'Don't you like having a bath?' asked Stephen.

'It reminds me of my childhood', said Bill. 'There were eleven of us and I was the youngest. We had no bathroom so, on a Friday night, we put a tin bath in front of the fire and filled it with hot water. What a job that was, too, heating it all on the stove. Then we all bathed in the same water and, as I was the youngest, I was last'.

'I bet the water was cold by then', said Stephen.

The old man nodded. 'Cold and full of scum from the coarse soap we used. I hated it!'

By the third week, Stephen was really looking forward to Friday. It surprised him how interesting it was talking to the old people and they always greeted the children with big smiles.

'What is the most interesting thing you remember from your childhood?' Stephen asked Margaret, the only person he hadn't yet spoken to.

Margaret looked at him with intense blue eyes. 'Well,' she said, in a quiet voice. 'It would be the time we happened to be in London when Lady Elizabeth Bowes-Lyon, the Queen Mother, as she is now, married the Duke of York in Westminster Abbey. It was in 1923 and I was just twelve and she looked ever so lovely'.

Stephen did some quick maths. 'You're ninety!' he said.

Margaret smiled. 'Next Friday', she said. 'I hope you're coming because they're putting on a special tea for me'.

Next Friday would be their last visit. Then it would be the turn of another six pupils. Stephen had two great ideas.

During the week, he told the rest of the group about Margaret's birthday, and everyone chipped in with some of their pocket money, so that when Friday came all six of them trooped into the sitting room and sang 'Happy Birthday' and Stephen presented Margaret with a bunch of flowers and some nice soap.

Margaret was so happy that she had to take off her glasses and wipe her eyes.

When Stephen and the others left, all the old people waved and told them to please visit again.

Stephen promised he would.

Usually after a PSD project they were expected to write an essay about their experiences. Stephen's other idea was that they do it in the form of a talk to the class. Him, making a speech!

He told them about all the interesting things he'd learned from the old people. The things they had done in their long lifetime and the memories they had. How they were interested in modern things, too, like computers and mobile phones and CDs, and about what they learned in school.

'Don't worry about not knowing what to talk about', said Stephen, taking his list of questions out of his pocket. 'I had these questions all ready but I never needed them once'.

End

Questions

1. What changed Stephen's attitude about going to see old people at Cranfield House?

2. How did he get his first opinion? How did he get his second opinion?

3. Have you, like Stephen, ever changed your mind about something through experience? *(Explain further, if necessary, then return to the question).*

4. From where do we get opinions? Are there different 'levels' of opinion? *(Level = strength of proof/evidence/truth).*

5. Stephen found out that having an opinion of something can be totally different from the experience. Has anyone got an example of that happening to them?

6. To 'serve' the old people, Stephen only had to 'be there'. He had to go to Cranfield House and he had to give his attention when he got there - in listening and speaking. Sometimes, people talk about 'being there' for someone. What does this mean, and has anyone got any examples?

Thought for the Day:

Life is dull if we just live by our old ideas all the time and don't open up to new opportunities. All we have to do is to be awake for them and be there! Look for new opportunities to serve someone.

Sarah was having a hard time at home. Her Mum had broken her leg, and Sarah was finding it hard to play a much bigger role in the family. What would be the consequences for the family if she failed?

Mum's Helper

Sarah shut the front door and swung her school bag onto her back. It felt as though half the day had gone already, she had been up since half past six. She hadn't done her maths homework either but she knew Mrs Barker would let her off. Making allowances, it was called.

'Hi, Sarah!' It was her best friend, Helen. 'Are you coming round tonight? We can watch the tennis on Sky'.

Sarah shook her head. 'Got to do some shopping after school and help mum with the dinner'.

Helen looked at her with pity. 'Oh, yeah. I forgot. How is your mum?'

Sarah shrugged. 'OK.'

'Did she break her leg, or what?' asked Helen.

'She had an operation on it and can't put any weight on it for two months', explained Sarah. 'And you can't do anything when you've got crutches and you're balancing on one leg'.

After school, as Sarah walked around the supermarket, she thought of Helen watching the tennis. They were both mad about tennis and loved to play but everything had changed since Mum had her operation.

Gran had taken time off work to look after her and her brother, Lee, while their mum had been in hospital but now there was no-one to help. If only their mum and dad hadn't split up. But she'd wished that a thousand times.

'Hello, Mum!' she called, letting herself in the front door. Angus, their Westie, flew at her ankles, barking, and she bent down to stroke him.

There was the thudding of crutches from upstairs and her mum's face appeared at the top of the stairs.

'Hello, love. I was just having a rest but I'm coming down now'. She promptly sat down and began to shuffle downstairs on her backside.

'I'll fetch your crutches, Mum'. Sarah smiled at the comical sight and her mum caught her eye. Then they both laughed. Angus barked again, joining in the fun.

'What an indignity', said Mum. 'But it's safer'.

Sarah made the dinner while her mum sat in the kitchen and told her what to do. Later, Lee came home from a friend's house and they all sat and ate. Then Sarah got the washing out of the machine and loaded it into the dryer.

'Lee's in bed', said her mum, hopping into the kitchen. 'I'm off too. I'm tired and my leg hurts. Try and do your homework, love, and be in bed by nine o'clock. Don't forget to feed Angus'.

Sarah kissed her mum goodnight and looked at her watch. It was already seven-thirty and she still had to do the washing up. It would be great to have a dish-washer like Helen's mum, but no chance of that.

That night, as Sarah climbed into bed and set her alarm for six-thirty, she thought about how strange it was to be responsible for all these domestic problems as if she were an adult - and to be the last one to go to bed. Things had certainly turned upside down.

She didn't have time to take Angus for a walk the next morning.

'Take him to the shops with you this afternoon', suggested her mum. Sarah pulled a face. She hated taking Angus to the shop. He was all right when he couldn't see her but as soon as she appeared at the check-out he would start to bark and jump up and down, nearly strangling himself with his lead. It was so embarrassing!

Sarah was late that morning and she had to run all the way to school. Lee had already gone with his friend, earlier, while she was helping her mum get dressed and make the beds. Now she ran, panting, into school just as the bell rang.

'Brought your racquet?' asked Helen.

Sarah clasped a hand on her mouth. How could she have forgotten? They were going to play at lunchtime and enter for the local 'Under 12s' tournament.

Helen was cross. 'I thought you loved tennis! We were going to be a doubles' team, remember?' She turned her back on Sarah and banged her schoolbag onto her desk.

'I do love tennis', said Sarah. 'But you know I have to help mum at the moment. There'll be time for tennis later, when she's better'.

'Huh', said Helen. 'I don't see why you can't have some time off'.

Sarah did consider asking her mum if she could play in the tournament on Saturday. Maybe Gran could come over, although she lived quite a long way away. Getting into the tournament was really important to her. She even had ambitions of playing at Wimbledon.

'Mum', she began after dinner that evening. 'I wondered if . . . '

Her mum looked up at her and Sarah noticed that her eyes were tired and red-rimmed. Maybe she had been crying which she sometimes did when she felt very low.

'What, love?'

'I wondered if your leg was hurting?'

Her mum nodded. 'It is a bit, but it's not that. I really feel bad that you have to take on all this responsibility and work at your age. At ten, you should be out with your friends, not doing housework. It's so frustrating, Sarah, not being able to do things. I could scream, sometimes. If only things had worked out better . . . '

She means between her and Dad, thought Sarah.

'It's all right, mum', she said.

But, what about the tennis tournament, thought Sarah. Well, she would still be under twelve next year. She could try then. She wished Helen could understand that when things cropped up in your life you couldn't just ignore them and hope that they would go away. They wouldn't. You had to get through them as best you could.

On Saturday morning Sarah was really tired and would have loved to lie in bed half the morning as she had done sometimes. She opened one eye and looked at her clock. Five past eight. She'd just have another ten minutes. Her mum usually did get her own breakfast so there was no real hurry.

Suddenly, there was a crash and a yell from downstairs and Sarah leapt out of bed and ran down the stairs two at a time, her heart thudding. In the kitchen her mum lay on the floor, groaning.

'My leg', she wailed. 'I tripped up over Angus and fell on my bad leg. It's agony'. Sarah stood looking at her mother's pale face, screwed up with pain. Should she help her up? What if the fall had messed up the operation and she had to go back into hospital?

'Phone Dr Harwood, love', gasped her mother.

Lee had come down, now, and stood whimpering in the doorway while Angus whined, sensing he was to blame.

Sarah ran into the living room and brought back a cushion to put under her mother's head. Then she ran to the phone and punched in the doctor's number. Being Saturday, she was referred to an emergency number and she explained what had happened.

Within twenty minutes an ambulance arrived and the paramedics carefully lifted mum onto the stretcher and took her out to the ambulance. After shutting Angus in the kitchen and making sure all the doors were locked, Sarah and Lee went to the hospital as well. They had quickly got dressed while they'd been waiting.

During the morning their mum had an X-ray and the consultant told them that everything was all right. She hadn't done any damage but must be more careful with the dog around. He asked if she had any help at home.

'Oh yes', she'd said, putting an arm around each of her children. 'I have very good help'.

End

Questions

1. Most of us usually see to our own needs first. Why was Sarah forced to see past her own needs?

2. Has anyone any examples of having a circumstance arise which forced them to see to the family's needs?

3. What would life have been like if Sarah hadn't seen to the family's needs?

4. *(Returning to those whose examples were given in question 2).* What would life have been like for your family if you had not met the need?

5. What did Sarah have to sacrifice *(give up)* to meet the needs of her family?

6. What do you think she gained by doing what she did?

Thought for the Day:

Sometimes difficult circumstances arise in families and we have to take on different roles according to what is needed. Whenever we give up something to do this, something else is gained. Don't only look at what you've lost - look at what you've gained!

Here is an ancient story from India. It was told to show the importance of serving others and also that we can learn such virtues by watching and learning from others. Conversely, it shows the importance of being a good example.

The Bamboo Jackets

Once, a king decided to have a big feast and invite as many people as possible from the surrounding villages. He got his servants to put up large tents and order the huge amount of food that would be necessary. The King called his most trusted adviser and gave him something special to order. The adviser was to tell no one of this.

The day of the feast arrived, and as the guests began to arrive they were startled to find that the king had laid down particular rules for this feast. All the guests were asked to put on a bamboo jacket. These were very awkward, and people struggled to get them on - all the time being tantalised by the smell of the delicious food that wafted out of the tents. At last, as each person finished putting on their jacket, there was a movement towards the great tents - everyone was feeling very hungry by now. As they seated themselves around the huge benches, piled high with food, the people began to realise that it would be impossible to eat wearing the jackets, the arms were just too stiff. The food could be picked up but not one person could bend their arm to get it to their mouth. However, the King had insisted - no jacket meant no food!

The King began to go around the different tents to see what was happening. The same scene met him in every tent. Dozens of hungry people who couldn't eat! Finally the King came to the tent where his wise men were seated. They also had on the bamboo jackets, but they had found a solution to the problem. Instead of trying to feed themselves, they were feeding each other, and so were busy enjoying the feast. Soon others also began to notice what was going on in the tent of the wise people, and began to copy. In this way everyone came to enjoy the feast of the King.

'If one could be made to understand that caring for oneself is bondage, while feeding others is freedom, then life would be easy for all . . . '

Shantanand Saraswati - Indian Philosopher

End

Questions

1. It seemed the King was playing a cruel joke on his subjects, but he was really wanting them to learn something about themselves. What do you think it was that he got his adviser to order?

2. Why might the King have wanted the bamboo jackets to be a surprise?

3. What do you think the King wanted his subjects to learn? *(Take a variety of answers; e.g. to look after others, see to the needs of others, share, not be greedy, etc).*

4. How were the wise men feeling? How were the others feeling?

5. What is it like if you have a meal with others - do you only see to yourself or are you awake to the needs of others? *(Take examples).*

6. Can you think of ways of putting what you have learned from the story into practice?

Thought for the Day:

Look for opportunities to look after someone else, even in doing something simple.

Beauty

What is 'beauty'? We have all experienced things that we call beautiful, but do we know much about the nature of beauty itself? As with many things, children learn about this concept by copying the examples and groups of things their parents (peers, teachers etc.) see as beautiful. At best therefore, this remains a partial understanding.

In the Platonic dialogue 'The Symposium', there is a conversation between Diotima (a Mantinean woman) and Socrates, in which Diotima seeks to lead Socrates to a deeper understanding of the nature of beauty. She shows that although there are different 'classes' of beauty, the actual experiencing of beauty in the individual, is the same in every case. To understand this, let us take for example a vase of flowers, a sunset, or a painting as examples of physical beauty. A tatty old book might not be physically beautiful, but if it contained the sonnets of Shakespeare, it could be considered to be beautiful in the sense of beauty of ideas. Moving to a more subtle level still, some systems of nature could be considered beautiful, for example the laws of geometry or the mathematical relationships between notes in the musical octave. It doesn't matter whether one agrees with the examples given - more important is to understand that these are examples at different 'levels' of beauty itself.

To begin to understand beauty itself, one has to observe what happens within when confronted by something beautiful - there is a connection between the external (that which is beautiful) and something internal. Students speak about an emotional response, that is, in connecting with something beautiful, they experience well-being and happiness.

The stories in this section seek to show that beauty can be experienced through different stimuli - things beautiful - but that to experience beauty fully one has to connect to it. (It is possible to walk through a beautiful park and not connect at all if the attention is on something else, such as a problem at work. No connection = no beauty). They also seek to illustrate that beauty is everywhere - the individual only has to find it. Socrates says that following the conversation with Diotima he determined to spend the rest of his life seeking beauty. What a nice approach to life!

'Beauty is reflected in the objects and in the observers who receive the beauty through the objects. If there were no beauty in the observer then he would not find beauty outside'.

Shantanand Saraswati - Indian philosopher

Molly was wrapped up in her own problems and worries. As she wakes up to the beauty that is around her she sees that in fact many of her worries were imaginary - she was turning lack of knowledge of something into a worry about it.

A Thing of Beauty

Molly kicked at a stone on the path and sent it skittering into the grass. She didn't want to be here. Here was boring. Here was the camping holiday with her parents and pain-in-the-neck brother Nicky. A whole week of nothing to do while her friends - not to mention Josh - had gone to Scotland with the school trip.

They were probably having a great time, she hardly dared think of it. She could cry with frustration when she thought of who Josh might be sitting next to on the coach.

Well, one thing was for sure - he wouldn't be thinking of her! He wouldn't have time to think about her and with girls outnumbering boys, what chance did she have of still being his girlfriend after the holidays?

Had her parents considered that? Did they understand just what it meant to be Josh Bentine's girl? Her, Molly Anderson, with mousy hair and fat legs? She wasn't exactly someone the boys fought over.

Molly scuffed along, raising dust which settled on her white trainers but she didn't care. Somewhere back there they would be getting up and making breakfast and wondering where she was. Let them wonder. Let them worry. They'd soon wish they had let her go on the school trip. She'd be miserable the whole week, spoil their holiday as they had spoilt her life.

She had lost Josh for sure.

Her toe caught on a rock embedded in the path and before she could regain her balance she was over, crashing down onto the grass at the side of the path. She fell hard onto her hip and lay there for a moment, eyes screwed up until the initial pain subsided. Now, on top of everything else, she would have a nice, fat bruise.

Molly opened her eyes but made no attempt to get up. She felt thoroughly fed up. She stared up at the sky, blue with a few high streaky clouds.

Something tickled her cheek and she turned her head to one side to see what it was. In front of her eyes was something bright yellow. She stared at the glorious colour, at the petals with frayed ends arranged in circles, darker orange in the centre. The petals were of uneven length yet the whole flower had a pleasing symmetry.

It was just a common dandelion. A weed. Yet how beautiful. She had never really looked closely at a flower before, and certainly not a dandelion. Why should just a weed be so lovely? Weeds were nuisance plants. People pulled them up and threw them away.

Slowly, Molly got to her feet and looked around her. There were dandelions everywhere like a golden carpet and in amongst them other flowers and grass. Beyond that the ground sloped away and she could see the sun glinting on a stream, way down in the valley. Beyond that the hills rose again.

Molly turned around. Behind her a dry stone wall meandered over the brow of the hill, broken in places, blotchy grey with lichen. Here and there small plants sprouted from between the stones.

The sun was growing warmer and Molly turned her face towards it and took a deep breath. She was suddenly aware of birds twittering in a nearby tree as if she'd had the sound turned off and had just turned up the volume.

It was really beautiful here. She longed to run down to the stream and paddle in the cool water. Feeling really hungry she turned back along the track, not scuffing her feet now but almost running.

The breeze ruffled her hair and she shook it behind her. Suddenly she felt beautiful. Josh had said he loved her hair. Wasn't there more to a person than what they looked like. You had to look deep inside to see the beauty - like the dandelion. Even weeds were beautiful.

Josh had said he would ring her and she had left her mobile in the tent.

Molly began to run.

End

Questions

1. What describes Molly's state at the start of the story?

2. What were the causes? Were they real or imaginary?

3. What began to happen to Molly after she had tripped up?
   (Her attention moved from being on ideas in her head to the world (beauty) around her. Further question the initial replies children give until they begin to appreciate this crucial point).

4. What changed when Molly moved her attention from her worries to the beauty around her?
   (Her feelings. She went from being miserable to being happy).

5. Sometimes we think something is beautiful and at other times the same thing appears not to be beautiful - or it is not noticed at all. Does the beautiful thing change or is it something else that changes?
   (This notion may take some questioning to make clear).

6. Exactly what is it that changes? *(The emotional response, not the beautiful thing itself).*

7. Sometimes we can be surrounded by beauty and not notice it. Why is that? *(An example may be useful - walking through a beautiful park and not being very aware of it).*
   (Concept - If attention is caught by ideas/thoughts 'in the head', the beauty capable of being appreciated through the senses is missed).

Thought for the Day:

When you notice you are caught up in a worry or idea in your head, give attention through the senses to the world around.

The main story is said to be part of a speech by Chief Seattle (more correctly 'Seathl') in 1854. There is much debate about the various versions of the speech, however, although we may never know exactly what he said, it is likely that the original was as eloquent as this, and the other subsequent versions.

How Can One Sell the Air?

Chief Seattle was the son of a Suquamish chief who lived in the area of Washington State in the nineteenth century. As a young man, he was renowned for his courage and daring, and was a natural leader of people. Seattle grew up in a time of great change in North America, during which the native Americans were facing challenges and changes to their way of life. Seattle grew up to be Chief, and in 1854 gave a famous speech to Isaac Stevens who was the Governor and Commissioner of Indian Affairs for the Washington Territories. Listen to part of Chief Seattle's speech and see if you think he had something important to say, and from which we can learn.

'The President in Washington sends word that he wishes to buy our land. But how can you buy and sell the sky, the land? The idea is strange to us. Every part of this earth is sacred to my people, every shining pine needle, every sandy shore, every mist in the dark woods, every meadow is holy in the memory and experience of my people. We are all part of the earth, and it is part of us. The perfumed flowers are our sisters. The bear, the deer, the great eagle, these are our brothers. Each ghostly reflection in the clear lakes tells of memories and events in the life of my people. The water's murmur is the voice of my father's father.

If we sell our land, remember that the air is precious to us, that the air shares its spirit with all the life it supports. The wind that gave our grandfather his first breath receives his last sigh. This we know. The earth does not belong to man: man belongs to the earth. All things are connected like the blood that connects us all. Man did not weave the web of life, he is merely a strand in it. Whatever he does to the web, he does to himself.

Your destiny is a mystery to us. What will happen when the buffalo are slaughtered? What will happen when the secret corners of the forest are heavy with scent of many men, and the view of the ripe hills is blotted with the talking wires? The end of living and the beginning of survival.

When the last red man vanishes with his wilderness, and his memory is only a shadow of a cloud moving across the prairie, will these shores still be here?

Will there be any spirit of my people left?

We love this earth as the new born loves its mother's heartbeat. So, if we sell you our land, love it as we have loved it; care for it as we have cared for it. Hold in your mind the memory of the land as it is as you receive it. Preserve the land for all children, and love it as God loves us all. One thing we know. There is only one God. No man, be he red man or white man, can be apart. We are brothers after all'.

End

Questions

1. Think about the content of the story. Can you think of any ways in which this story could be considered beautiful? *(Children may speak of the beauty of nature that is described, the beauty of the language, the beauty of ideas, and so on. Accept their answers, but do not give any of your own.)*

2. Sometimes things can be beautiful not because we can appreciate the beauty through the senses by seeing, hearing, or touching it, but because we can appreciate beautiful ideas with our mind. Did Chief Seattle have any ideas that you think are beautiful? *(Take answers and ask the children to give reasons for their choices).*
   This is a difficult concept *(especially from memory)* so if no answers are forthcoming give some examples of your own and ask if anyone agrees with any of them, and why.

3. Is the language beautiful? *(Give some examples by re-reading some small sections that appeal to you).*
   What effect does this have on us? *(For example, it draws us to connect more with the meaning, it makes us want to hear more, we have a greater emotional response to what is being said).*

4. Have you heard any ideas which you think are useful to us today? *(Having a written copy of the speech to explore at greater length would be a useful follow-up for older children. They could explore the same questions, and also look for a philosophical question themselves, on which to base an enquiry.)*

Thought for the Day:

Looking after the world is the duty of everyone. See if you can notice ways in which you can play your part in this.

We all have those seemingly insignificant events that remain in memory for a lifetime. A kind action, something someone says to us. This story portrays such an event, and shows how a small kindness can have a large effect.

The Lists

Cast:	Narrator, Mrs Dylon, Pauline, Gareth, Laila, David's Dad, David's Mum.
Narrator:	One morning Mrs Dylon, Year 5's teacher, hands out a sheet of paper to everyone and tells them to write down the names of all their classmates and leave a line between each name.
Mrs Dylon:	'Now, I want you to write down the nicest thing you can about each person'.
Narrator:	It takes the rest of that lesson. That evening Mrs Dylon takes a sheet of paper for each pupil and writes down everything that had been said about them. The next morning she hands out the lists. Soon, everyone is smiling and looking around at each other.
Pauline:	'Wow! Am I really like that?'
Gareth:	'I never realised people thought that about me'.
Laila:	'It feels so good to be liked'.
Narrator:	Mrs Dylon never knows what happened to the lists after that. Whether the pupils discuss them or show them to their parents she never hears. Nothing more is said about them. Several years later she hears that one of her pupils, David, who has joined the army, has been killed in a conflict overseas. Mrs Dylon goes to his funeral. All his family and friends are in the church. Then, afterwards, they all go to David's parents' house. His father comes up to Mrs Dylon.
David's Dad:	'Are you Mrs Dylon, David's teacher?'
Mrs Dylon:	*(nodding)* 'Yes'.
David's Dad:	*(reaching into his pocket)* 'I want to show you something, Mrs Dylon'.

71

Narrator:	David's Dad takes out his wallet and opens it.
David's Dad:	'They found this on David when he was killed. We thought you might recognise it'.
Narrator:	David's Dad takes out a ragged old piece of paper. It is grubby and falling apart and has obviously been folded and patched up with sellotape many times. Mrs Dylon knows it is the piece of paper which lists all the good things people had said about David.
David's Mum:	'Thank you very much for doing that. As you can see, David treasured it very much'.
Narrator:	David's old classmates gather around.
Gareth:	'I still have my list at home in my desk'.
Pauline:	*(reaching into her bag)* 'Here's mine. I carry it with me all the time. Look how worn it is'.
Laila:	'I think we all saved our lists. There were times when I had no confidence in myself at all and was feeling really low. Then I would take out my list and read it. What a boost it gave me'.
Narrator:	Everyone nods. There is a moment of silence as everyone remembers David. Mrs Dylon wipes her eyes. It had just been an experiment and one which she had carried on over the years. Now she could see that it was the best thing she had ever done.

End

Questions

1. Spend a moment or two thinking about what we say to other people. Try to remember the last nice thing and last unpleasant thing you said about someone.

2. Think about the last time someone said something nice to you. What was the effect? *(What did you feel?)*
   Can you give any examples?

3. Why do you think Mrs Dylan asked the children to write the lists?

4. Why did lots of people keep their lists?

5. What effect did the lists have? Why did they have that effect?

6. Laila said, 'When I had no confidence in myself, or I was feeling low, I would take out my list and read it. What a boost it gave me'. Why do you think it had that effect?

Thought for the Day:

If we choose it, the way we treat each other can be beautiful. Remember that all our words and actions have an effect. Choose to say and do those things which have a good effect.

The traditional story of Beauty and the Beast reminds us that there is more to beauty than just the outward physical. It reminds us to look beyond the obvious before making judgements about things. There is also beauty of conduct - the way we behave, with all the associated feelings and attitudes.

Beauty and the Beast

There was once a merchant who had three daughters. Just before he set off on a business trip, he asked them what they would like him to bring back for them.

'A necklace, please, father', said the eldest.

'A gold chain for me, please', said the middle daughter.

But the youngest daughter, whose name was Bella, just shook her head. 'I want nothing, father', she said. 'Just bring yourself back, safely'.

'Nonsense', said the father. 'I want to bring you a gift'.

Bella thought for a moment. 'Then I would like a rose, please'.

The merchant went about his business and he bought the necklace and the gold chain for his two eldest daughters but decided to leave the rose until last so that it would be fresh. Then he forgot about it.

He was almost home when he suddenly remembered the rose and started to look around for somewhere to buy one. As he turned a corner he saw a beautiful garden and there, in the centre of a circle of lawn, was a rose bush laden with blooms.

The merchant got off his horse, walked through the great wrought iron gates and stepped onto the grass circle. Surely the owners wouldn't miss one rose. He chose a deep red rosebud and plucked it off the bush.

CRASH! A loud noise filled his ears and there, in front of him, stood a hideous beast. Its eyes were red and glaring, its lips curled back from a cluster of pointed grey teeth. Three horns protruded from the green, scaly, skin of its head and long strings of saliva dripped from its black tongue.

'Thief !' growled the beast. 'You are stealing my roses'.

The merchant explained about the gift for his daughter.

'That is no excuse! Your life is the forfeit'.

'Oh please', begged the merchant. 'Please spare my life. I have three daughters to support and care for. I am really sorry for stealing your rose'.

'I shall spare your life on one condition', said the beast. 'Seven days from now you must bring me your youngest daughter'.

The merchant arrived home to a great welcome from his daughters and gave them their gifts, but the youngest daughter could tell that something was wrong and he was unhappy. Eventually he told her about the beast and the condition it imposed to spare his life.

'I will go, father', said Bella, bravely. So the next day they set off.

Like her father, Bella was shocked when she saw the beast and could hardly bare to look at his ugliness. The beast told the merchant that he could visit Bella every week and that he meant her no harm.

Bella was shown to her luxurious rooms and over the next few weeks she had everything she wanted. She only had to ask for something out loud and some invisible servants brought it to her. The beast hardly ever appeared. Bella spent the long days walking in the vast gardens or reading books.

It sounds wonderful, doesn't it? But Bella began to get lonely. Apart from seeing her father or sisters once a week she never saw anyone else at all.

On one of the rare times when the beast appeared, Bella asked him to walk with her in the garden. Then she told him about her father and sisters and of her mother who had died when she was a child.

Bella talked more and more with the beast. He was so kind and thoughtful that she lost her fear of him and the walks in the garden became a daily event that she looked forward to. She told him about her life and her interests and her hopes.

Then one day the beast did not appear. Bella felt really disappointed and she waited an hour before going to look for him. She searched the whole of the great house, looking in rooms she had never been in before, but she couldn't find the beast.

Then, as she passed an open window, she heard cries and groans of pain coming from the front garden. Down the stairs she ran, through the front door and out to the very rosebush from which her father had plucked the rose. There was the beast, lying on the ground with blood pouring from a great wound in his chest. He was gasping for breath and twisting in agony.

Bella fell on her knees beside him. 'What's happened? Who did this to you?'

'The people of the village', whispered the beast. 'They think I am evil. They don't like me living here'.

Frantically, she tore off a piece of her skirt, and tried to staunch the flow of blood.

'Oh, please don't die, beast', she wept. 'Please don't die. I love you so much'.

There was a flash of bright light and suddenly a prince stood before her, his handsome face smiling with love and gratitude.

'You have broken the spell', he said.

Bella wiped her eyes and stared at him in bewilderment.

'I was enchanted by an evil magician', explained the prince. 'And the spell could only be broken if a maiden declared her love for me of her own free will. You did that. Ugly as I was, you still loved me'.

Bella and the prince were married and . . . lived . . . happily . . . ever . . . after!

End

Questions

1. What do you think made Bella say she would go to live at the Beast's house?

2. Was this decision brave or foolish? *(Children should give reasons for their opinion).*

3. How did Bella's relationship with the beast change? What was the cause of the change?

4. When Bella said she loved the beast, what do you think it was that she loved?

5. Has anyone ever changed what they thought about someone once they were better known? *(Examples are useful, but not if they are too personal or critical).*

Thought for the Day:

Try not to be critical or make judgements about others just on first impressions or what they look like. Look for what is behind the obvious.

Beauty may be shown through different kinds of examples. The beauty is the same but the medium is different. In this story, Ian Mackenzie realises that the emotional response, the enjoyment, of the beauty is the same whatever the cause.

By the Loch

Ian Mackenzie pulled into the small parking area and switched off the car's engine. Then he got out and stood for a moment, looking out over the loch. He passed here a dozen times a year but never failed to stop and spend a few moments enjoying the scene.

He found a place on the grassy slope and sat down, hugging his knees and breathing in the fresh clean air.

The loch was still, like a mirror image of the surrounding hills, darkening purple as the sun went down.

There was no sound, except, if he really listened, the occasional cry of a bird.

Sometimes when he came here the loch was angry and turbulent and black clouds skudded across the sky. Other times it silently reflected the brilliant white blanket of snow which covered the land.

But in all moods the loch was beautiful. Breathtaking. A place of peace which never changed despite what was happening in the rest of the world. Ian watched as the sky became streaked with pink and red as if the artist had gone mad with his brush.

He was not alone, either. Several other people were sitting watching the sunset too, and one couple was walking along the shore. A woman sat with a small child playing on the grass beside her. Every now and then he would totter a little too far and then she would reach out and grasp his arm to draw him back to safety.

As the sun went down, the people became just dark silhouettes and Ian felt a sort of companionship with them. A surge of emotion welled up inside himself and the problems in his life seemed to vanish. As usual, the beauty of this place had acted like a tonic, the best medicine in the world.

The sun slowly disappeared behind the hills and the red and orange streaks dissolved into a rosy glow. People were beginning to stand up and climb back up the slope. A cool breeze suddenly ruffled the grass and shattered the reflection on the loch.

A gurgle of childish laughter made Ian look over to the woman and her child. She was jigging him up and down on her knee and chanting a little rhyme though Ian couldn't hear the words. The child was squealing with laughter. Ian smiled to himself and felt the same sense of elation that he had done watching the sunset. Here was another kind of beauty - the love between a parent and a child.

He got up, stiffly, and brushed the grass off his clothes. Then he strolled back to his car with a light heart.

End

Questions

1. Why did Ian Mackenzie stop by the loch that day?

2. Ian stopped there often because he always found it beautiful, but what else did he always find went along with the beauty?

3. Ian suddenly noticed that other people were also silently watching the beautiful sunset. Why do you think he found 'a sort of companionship with them'?

4. Have you ever been looking at something beautiful and had the sort of feeling that Ian had - can you describe it to us?

5. How did Ian feel when he saw the mother playing with her young child? What was familiar to him about that feeling?

6. Think of different kinds of beauty that you have observed and try to remember how you felt in each case. Any examples? *(Try to get the children to see that there are different kinds of beauty, not just different examples of the same kind. For example there are beautiful things (sunset, flowers, statue), beautiful ideas, beautiful actions).*

Thought for the Day:

Open up to the world around you. Observe the beauty all around you, and also how that makes you feel. You can see that beauty and enjoy that feeling every day if you choose!

Patience

'Patience is a virtue', so the old saying goes. Curiously, it is sometimes almost the antithesis which is true in some quarters today, where to be impatient or short tempered almost becomes 'fashionable' or a statement! The growing phenomena of road rage *(and the like)* or the way children use impatience as an excuse for their behaviour, also points to the loss of tolerance and the practice of patience.

The natural state of human beings is one of constancy, so to be patient is to move towards that natural state and is quite 'lawful'. We are centred, secure and happy in that state. To be impatient is to move away from that steady state and not natural. This brings with it agitation, and sometimes rage, anger and the like. It is important for children to understand this.

Patience can be practised in many different situations, and these stories try to portray some of them. Patience may be needed to overcome a difficulty or handicap, to achieve an ambition, or to deal with a difficult situation - the context may change but the quality remains the same.

Emily has to use patience in overcoming a lifelong fear of dogs. Gradually, she learns to overcome the fear, and little by little gains the confidence to be calm in the presence of a dog.

The Girl Who Was Afraid of Dogs

Emily was afraid of dogs. It wasn't that she disliked them, but she was absolutely petrified of them. At ten, she and her friends were old enough to walk to school, but Emily always asked her Mum to go with her, in case they met any dogs along the way. Even dogs on leads or behind garden walls frightened her. If someone with a dog came down the street, she had to cross the road.

It had all started, her mum explained, when she was a baby out in her buggy and a big, boisterous dog had barked and then ran up and licked her face. The dog had meant no harm but it had given her a fright.

Of course, Emily knew that most dogs were friendly, but that didn't make any difference. But her fear was a nuisance and she was teased about it. It was difficult to keep a thing like that secret and sometimes other kids would make barking noises at her and call her a baby for having her mother walk her to school.

She often missed out on birthday parties and sleepovers because a lot of her friends had dogs. Even on short visits, she had to ask if the dog could be shut outside or inside, depending on where they were playing, and all the time she was alert, worrying that it would escape. It was ruining her life.

At last, she decided she had to do something about it.

'I'll take you to a therapist', said her mum. 'There's one advertised in the paper. Eighty per cent success rate with phobias, it says'.

That wasn't too encouraging. What if she was one of the twenty per cent who couldn't ever be cured?

Emily's Mum made an appointment and one Saturday morning they went along to Mr Penrose's house.

'Right, Emily', said Mr Penrose. 'I have a friend who is going to take his dog to the park today. It will be on a lead the whole time so you needn't worry'.

As they got into the car, Emily could feel her heart thudding. This was really scary.

At the park, Emily strolled with Mr Penrose along the path to a quiet area near some thick shrubbery.

'Marcia should be waiting here', said Mr Penrose. 'Are you ready, Emily?'

Emily nodded. Then she saw the dog and stopped.

'I can't go any further,', she said.

'Not just a couple of steps?' asked the therapist.

Her hands were sweaty now and she wiped them on her jeans. Then she forced one foot forward, then the other. This was the closest she had ever been to a dog. She looked at it. It was a black poodle. It was looking at her and wagging its tail.

Suddenly, along the path bounded another dog. Emily squealed and hid behind her mum.

'I want to go home', she whispered. She was trembling all over.

'Enough for today', Mr Penrose said. 'You've done well, Emily'.

For the next three weeks the therapist talked to Emily and encouraged her to go closer and closer to the dog, but he never pushed her too hard. She had to want to do it herself.

And she did. However long it took she was determined to conquer her fear.

The following week Marcia brought the dog to Emily's own garden.

She had lain awake half the night worrying about it, yet she would progress to touching the dog, even if it took weeks.

It sat beside Marcia at the end of the garden and looked, inquisitively, at Emily, gradually approaching. Step by step she went. The dog wagged its tail and looked at her, tongue hanging out. It looked as though it was laughing.

'On a scale of one to ten', said Mr Penrose, 'how much anxiety do you feel?'

'Eight', said Emily. They'd used this method several times.

'Can you come a little nearer?'

'I'm not sure'. Emily stepped nearer.

'How much now?' asked the therapist.

'Six', said Emily.

'You see, it's coming down. Your fear reaches a peak but then always comes down'.

Emily took another step. Now she was only a couple of metres away from the dog, who was straining to get up and greet her. She could smell it. She could feel her heart beating fast. She had to do it. She had to touch the dog. If she didn't do it now she would never do it.

As if in slow motion, Emily took another step forward and then stretched her hand out. She stretched out her fingers nearer and nearer to the black curly coat.

Then she touched it! She felt the springy, curly fur. Gradually, over the next half hour, she was able to bend and stroke the dog's head and tickle its tummy.

Later, when her Dad came home, there was a celebration.

'You were very brave, Emily', he said. 'Well done'.

It took some time for Emily's fear to go completely but whenever she met a dog she knew, she would talk to it and stroke it and play with it. Now she could walk to school on her own and go to friends' houses.

Finally, she said the words her parents had never thought to hear.

'Can I have a dog, please?'

Her patience and perseverance had paid off.

End

Questions

1. Many people have fears of things. Sometimes they can't explain why they have the fear, but it still seems very real. Why do you think Emily would want to try to overcome her fear?

2. What was the first thing she had to do in overcoming her fear? *(Make a decision about it).*

3. Why do you think the therapist said Emily had done well when she was still trembling and hiding behind her Mum?

4. Emily was patient in gradually becoming more confident with the poodle, until at last she could stroke and tickle it. Has anyone an example of being patient in overcoming a fear?

5. How did people who didn't have your fear react to you? How did you feel about that? *(Explore different reactions of people to the person with the fear, and how that person felt).*

6. How did Emily feel about herself when she was able to touch the dog? Why? How did you *(speaking to the person from question 4)* feel about yourself? Why?

Thought for the Day:

We may not always understand our fears, but with patience we can overcome them, although sometimes we need the help of someone else, just as Emily did.

Patience can be used not only for one's own benefit, but also for that of others, as Jamie finds out in helping his brother. Curiously, he finds there is also something in it for him!

Learning to Swim

Jamie was a champion swimmer. In fact, his ambition was to swim in the Olympics one day. He competed in all the swimming competitions at his local sports centre. Like a duck in water, his mum always said.

And she, Jamie thought, was like a cat in water. She hated it. In fact cats could swim if they had to, whereas she couldn't. She often said that her brother had ducked her when they were children and she'd hated it ever since.

Today, Mum was taking Jamie and his young brother Brad to the swimming pool. Jamie had a practice session later.

'Teach me to swim', said Brad, in the car. He was just five and had recently started school. 'I want to swim like you, Jamie'.

Jamie laughed. 'You're afraid of getting your face wet. You always cry. You have to put your face under water to swim properly'.

'I will put my face in', said Brad, but he looked at their mother, apprehensively.

When they got to the pool the two boys went to put on their trunks and their mum went to sit in the spectators' seats.

Jamie really wanted to dive straight into the big pool and carve swiftly through the water with his strong crawl. There weren't many people and the empty lanes looked really tempting.

'Another time, Brad', he said.

His brother pouted. 'Please, Jamie. I want to swim like you'.

What if he did teach Brad? What if Brad became a better swimmer than him?

Reluctantly he gave in.

'Okay'. Jamie went to the small pool and slid in off the side. Brad hesitated on the edge. He looked up at their mum, then back at the water.

'Come on', said Jamie, impatiently. 'Do you want me to teach you or not?'

'Don't force him', called out Mum. 'You might scare him'.

Jamie wished he'd said no at the beginning.

Brad ran to the steps and climbed down into the water. It came up to his waist.

'Right', said Jamie. 'Hold on to the edge and kick your legs. Like this'.

But Brad couldn't get his feet off the bottom.

Jamie sighed. 'You can't swim with your feet on the bottom', he said. This was wasting time. He thought of grabbing Brad's legs and lifting them up. He'd heard of people who threw young children into the pool so that they had to swim. That way they learned quickly.

'I'll hold you around the waist', he said. 'You'll be all right'.

'I might sink', wailed Brad. Jamie saw the fear in his brother's face and he softened a little.

'No, you won't. I won't let you sink'.

Slowly, Brad lifted one foot off the bottom, then the other. Finally his body floated while he held the side of the pool. By the end of the session he could do it without Jamie holding him.

But then he let go with one hand to wave to Mum and his face went under and he got a mouthful of water and came up crying. Mum came running down and lifted him out.

This is hopeless, thought Jamie. Crying just because he got a mouthful of water.

'Brad', said Jamie. 'Don't be such a baby. I sometimes get a mouthful of water too'.

'He got a fright', said Mum, soothingly stroking Brad's wet hair.

'I got a fright', echoed Brad.

'I'm going to practice', muttered Jamie. He was fed up with both of them. He didn't care if Brad never learned to swim. What did it matter?

Nevertheless, the next week he began to teach him again. During the week he had remembered being afraid himself. It had been when he had dived to the bottom to get his locker key, which had slipped off his wrist. It had been quite shallow but had seemed a long way down and he had almost panicked. The water had gurgled loudly and had stung his eyes and he had wanted to breathe. His lungs had been bursting. Then there was the time he'd suddenly found himself out of his depth . . .

'Now you have to learn what to do with your arms', he said to Brad.

Brad started churning his arms around like windmills, slapping the water with open palms.

'No, no', said Jamie. 'Your hands have to be paddles and push the water away. Like this'.

He cupped one hand and pushed it through the water. Brad tried again.

'That's better. Now, I'll hold you and you try to swim'.

Later they practised putting their heads under water. Jamie showed Brad how to hold his nose until he got used to it and the little boy managed to dunk his head under quickly and come up smiling.

'Very good', said Jamie.

Soon Brad could swim on his own for a few strokes and the day he did a whole width Jamie felt really proud. Brad's style wasn't great but Jamie could work on that.

All his patience had been worth it. Maybe he'd even persuade Mum to come and have a lesson.

End

Questions

1. Why didn't Jamie want to teach Brad to swim? *(Look for several reasons).*

2. Why do you think he changed his mind?

3. Using the evidence in the story, would you say Jamie was patient or not patient? *(Ensure that children give reasons for their point of view).*

4. How did Jamie feel, having taught Brad to swim? How did this compare to how he felt at the beginning of the story?

5. What are some things that would make you patient in dealing with a younger brother or sister? What are some things that would make you impatient?

Thought for the Day:

When you find yourself feeling impatient with someone, try to look for the reasons you are feeling like that. When we understand something it changes our feelings.

In a world of quick fixes and instant solutions, patience is sometimes needed to see a task through to conclusion. This is an important attitude to develop, as it affects an individual's approach to, and success in life. Those who give in at the first hurdle to any problem have the idea of failure reinforced, leading to low self-esteem. Such individuals avoid challenging situations. Conversely, just having the idea of patiently persevering with something, leads to more success, higher self-esteem and a generally more positive cycle.

Paul's Boat

Paul loved boats but the only one he had been on was the ferry going to France. He dreamed of joining the Merchant Navy or sailing, single handed, around the world. He wished he had been a sailor long ago in those great, wooden, sailing ships exploring all corners of the world. He pictured himself climbing the rigging to furl the sails, the ship tossing beneath him, salty spray in his face.

Now, the first step in this dream had happened. He and his family had moved into a house with a river running behind. It wasn't a major river, in fact it was only about five metres wide and one metre deep, just a tributary really. But, it was a start.

Now, he had decided to build a boat so he could sail on the river. He couldn't wait. They'd hardly been in the new house a week and Paul was out looking for pieces of wood suitable for his boat. He'd seen some discarded planks on some waste ground. He'd have the boat built in no time. It shouldn't be difficult, after all, wood floated.

All Saturday he worked. He drew a simple design for a dinghy and rummaged in his Dad's garage for a saw, hammer and nails.

Soon he'd be sailing on the river, exploring as far as he could. He'd give the boat a name and might even put a mast and sails on it to catch the wind. Ah - he mustn't forget some oars to begin with.

There was still another week left of the summer holidays. Plenty of time.

For the next two days he sawed and hammered. Sometimes his Mum or Dad or older brother, Robin, came to look.

'How's it going, son?' his Dad would ask. Robin had no interest in boats and just laughed.

By the third day Paul had to admit that it didn't look much like a boat. The bits of wood were all different lengths and thicknesses and were not curved of course. Even as just a square raft with sides it looked odd and he was afraid to try it out to see if it floated. Besides, he didn't want a raft, he wanted a boat.

He sat, glumly, head in hands, staring at the silly contraption he'd built. Some of the nails were too long and protruded dangerously through the wood.

Paul got up, wandered down to the river and squatted at the water's edge staring into it. He'd really expected to be sailing on it by now.

'Not working on the boat, son?' It was his Dad, who'd come up behind him.

Paul shook his head. 'It's no good', he said. 'It's silly'.

'Well, you tried', said his Dad. 'But to do anything properly you need the right material. Boat-building is a skilled craft, not just a matter of nailing a few bits of wood together'.

Paul nodded.

'Don't give up', said Dad. 'Just wait. Have patience and I'll see what I can do. But it won't be finished before the end of the holidays. You know what I've always said - if you're going to do a job, do it properly'.

A few days later, Paul's Dad brought home a roll of thick paper and handed it to him.

It was the plans for a boat. Proper plans! Paul studied it carefully. It was very detailed showing all the measurements and required pieces of wood, even the type of wood.

Paul began the Autumn term at his new school and made some friends, even one who was also keen on sailing who offered to help with the boat-building.

Paul's Dad bought the timber and other materials needed and agreed to leave the car parked in the drive so that the boat could be built in the garage.

First, they built the frame. Then the sides. The cracks between the pieces had to be sealed with special stuff to make them water-tight. Then they put in the seats.

Christmas came and Paul got a pair of oars as a present. Still the boat-building went on. Finally, by March, there was only the varnishing to do, and another important feature. To find a name for her!

Paul racked his brains for something appropriate.

'Well', said Mum, coming to inspect the boat. 'You thought you could build a boat in a couple of days but it's taken six months. All your patience and hard work have been worth it, haven't they?' She smiled at Paul.

'That's it!' said Paul. 'I'll call her Patience!'

Dad nodded. 'A good name too', he said. 'Many famous ships had similar sorts of names. Just think of Captain Cook's 'Endeavour' and 'Resolution' and Nelson's 'Victory'.

'Can we launch her too, Dad, like a real ship?'

'Yes, but not with champagne. We don't want all that broken glass in the river', said Dad, with a smile.

So, they painted 'Patience' on her bows and gave her three coats of special varnish.

At last, she was finished, and Paul stood back and looked at the boat with pride. He and his friend, Rick, and Robin and Dad carried the boat down to the river for the launching.

It had taken a long time, but when Paul thought back to his first efforts at boat-building he smiled to himself. How silly he'd been. How impatient. This had all been worth waiting for.

End

Questions

1. What was the motivating idea that started Paul building a boat?

2. Can you describe his feelings *(emotions)* at the start, which made him want to get started straight away?

3. What do you think Paul's Dad thought about the first boat?

4. Why do you think he let Paul carry on with the boat?

5. How did Paul feel by the third day - what were his feelings then? What had he realised?

6. Do you think Paul's emotions were different during the building of the second boat to those during the building of the first *(as in question 2)*? Why? What were his feelings in the end?

Thought for the Day:

Things that are worthwhile often need patience to 'see them through' or complete them successfully. Try to notice the times when you are having patience to complete a task.

This story shows the link between patience and perseverance and that in some circumstances they can be two sides of the same coin. Robert the Bruce is inspired by the patience and perseverance of a spider and determines to adopt the same attitude.

Robert the Bruce and the Spider

A sharp, cold, wind howled at the entrance of the cave and the man shivered and pulled his cloak around him. He could hear the sound of the sea crashing against the rocks not far away.

Whatever was he, King Robert the Bruce of Scotland, doing here in this cave, alone, except for two or three of his loyal friends?

He moved further into the cave and sat down, his back against the rocky wall, and he began to think.

Would they ever defeat the English and drive them out of Scotland? Would the Scots ever be free people, independent and able to run their own lives?

He thought of his compatriot, William Wallace, who had been executed the previous year fighting for his country. He thought of his wife and young daughter imprisoned in an English castle, and of his three brothers, also killed.

The year was 1306 and Scotland had just suffered yet another defeat, at the Battle of Falkirk.

King Edward I of England was a tough enemy and Robert the Bruce was being hunted down by him. He was angry that Robert had been crowned King when there was already a king on the Scottish throne, one chosen by him.

If Robert was caught, would he suffer the same terrible fate as William Wallace, who had been hung, drawn and quartered?

Robert shuddered, and not only from the cold this time. He was only 32 years old but the future looked bleak. He hung his head in despair and cried out in anguish.

A sudden spatter of rain blowing in made him look up again. His eyes had grown accustomed to the gloom now and in front of him he saw a spider hanging from a single thread of web.

As he watched, the spider swung upwards, trying to fix its web to the roof of the cave. Each time it swung, it was unable to reach but it kept trying. Four, five, six times the spider swung, sometimes almost reaching the roof but always falling back.

But it didn't give up. Never once did it appear to pause and wonder whether it was worth trying again.

Robert watched, fascinated. For a time it took his mind off his own worries.

When the spider finally succeeded, Robert cheered and laughed out aloud and watched as the small creature began to weave its web. Then he jumped to his feet and picked up his sword, brandishing it in the air just as his companions returned from their small hunting expedition, each holding a rabbit.

'You are in good spirits, Sire', exclaimed Sir James Douglas. 'Is it the sight of the supper we have brought you?'

Robert shook his head and pointed to the spider.

'If a small creature such as this can show unlimited patience in achieving its goal, surely a man can do the same! From now on, gentlemen, my motto will be: 'If at first you don't succeed, try, try, try again!'

And so, over the next eight years, King Robert the Bruce and his armies fought to win back many Scottish Castles and lands which had been in the hands of the English.

Finally, on 24th June, 1314, against all the odds, he defeated the English armies, now under the leadership of King Edward II, at the famous Battle of Bannockburn, and Stirling castle was once more in Scottish hands.

Some years later, Scotland became a free and independent country. Robert the Bruce was a hero, and all because of a spider who showed him that if you want to do something badly enough, you should keep trying and never give up.

End

Questions

1. Why do you think the spider kept trying, again and again, to connect the thread? *(Take a range of answers).*

2. If, sometimes, we give up when something doesn't work out the first time, what is it that makes us give up? *(An idea of one kind or another).*

3. Does anyone have an example of this, not completing or succeeding in something because you gave up easily? *(Hear the example/s and try to elicit, through questioning, why the person gave up).*

4. Has anyone an example of being patient in order to succeed at something?

5. Can you think of any other creatures that might show patience through their behaviour?

Thought for the Day:

One of the meanings of patience given in the dictionary is 'being calm in relation to time and processes'. Some things take time to do them properly. See if you can notice whether you stay calm when something takes time to finish.

This well known fable shows that having patience with something means giving a measured and focussed response, and is not to do with seeking a solution through an erratic, irrational expenditure of energy.

The Tortoise and the Hare
(Aesop's Fable)

Hare was always making fun of Tortoise.

'You're so slow', he would say. 'Can't you move faster than that? Look how fast I can run'. And he would leap away over the fields in a flurry of grey fur.

Sometimes, Hare laughed at Tortoise's shell.

'It's silly carrying your house on your back. Why not leave it at home?' Then he would roar with laughter at his joke.

Tortoise said nothing. One thing tortoises have is patience and he knew that one day he would show Hare that patience and determination were more important than just speed.

One morning, Hare was being particularly annoying, and Tortoise's patience ran out. Just for a moment though, just long enough for him to say, 'I bet I can beat you in a race to the farmhouse'.

Hare fell about, laughing. 'Done!' he said. 'I'll give you half an hour's start, or even half a day'. He chuckled again.

All the animals gathered around to watch and Horse drew a line in the dirt with his hoof.

'Ready, steady, go!' shouted Horse.

Off they went, Hare leaping and bounding, Tortoise just plodding.

Hare came to some juicy dandelions and stopped for a nibble. He had plenty of time.

Tortoise plodded on. He didn't try to rush.

Hare met some of his friends in the field and stopped to play. He wasn't worried. No tortoise could ever beat him.

Tortoise plodded on. He had waited a long time to teach Hare a lesson.

When the sun grew hot Hare sat down under the big oak tree for a while and nodded off to sleep.

Tortoise plodded on. Past Hare he went. He didn't stop for a rest. He didn't stop for food. He was going to win this race.

Hare woke up. He didn't know that Tortoise had passed him. Now he was too hot to run so he just ambled along, confidently.

Tortoise plodded on. He wasn't hot. His shell shaded his body. Now he could see the barn. Was he going to win, or would Hare come leaping past at the last minute? Tortoise didn't stop to look round. He would get there.

It was only as Tortoise plodded the last few steps towards the barn, that Hare spotted him, a small moving dot in the distance ahead. He sprang forward, but it was too late.

Tortoise had been determined and nothing had distracted him along the way. He had won the race and at last silenced Hare's teasing, forever. It had been worth waiting for this moment.

End

Questions

1. Tortoise's patience stopped for a moment and he challenged Hare to a race. Has anyone ever had an occasion when you were being patient, then *(as is sometimes said)* your patience ran out? *(Take examples).*

2. Can anyone *(who gave an example)* say why their patience stopped? What made you change?

3. Can patience actually 'run out'? What actually happens? *(An idea or attitude changes).*

4. Can you describe the differences in how the hare and the tortoise each approached the race? Think about their attitudes. *(Take descriptions).*

5. What sort of attitude would you say was connected with patience?

6. What do people mean when they say 'Patience is a virtue'?

Thought for the Day:

Patience is a very good quality. Try to have patience with people and situations. If you find yourself not being patient, try to see what it is that is stopping you.

KNOWLEDGE

Knowledge is the state of knowing. Knowledge of this and that brings with it pleasure or pain depending on how one identifies with what is known. I know this and it makes me happy or I know that and I am sad. True knowledge, or knowledge of the true, somehow rises above that, leading to a state of equilibrium. Knowledge actually implies true knowledge, some would argue that it is impossible to know something which is not true.

Knowledge is limitless and always available - in the present moment. The function of knowledge is to illuminate. We all see that when we 'know' something - it is as if a light is switched on, it is understood. Unfortunately, when this happens, it is all too easy to claim the knowledge for oneself, and so knowledge becomes power. Knowledge is for sharing.

'Know Thyself' was carved over the entrance to the Delphic oracle. Socrates would poke fun at the sophists who asked questions about the universe before *(he said)* they knew about themselves. These stories seek to show that knowledge starts with knowledge of oneself and moves out from there. The use *(or mis-use)* of knowledge is also explored, as are the implications for acting on partial knowledge.

Jesus said, 'Whosoever knows the All, but fails to know himself lacks everything'.

Gospel according to Thomas

Knowledge is pretty useless if it is just information or facts in the mind. Knowledge is useful when it has a practical purpose - when it is made real, or realised. Jack has a reputation for being 'brainy' but Marty is able to use his knowledge in a practical way. Beth has knowledge of people (is emotionally intelligent) and uses this to keep everyone calm in a scary situation.

Marooned

Cast:	Narrator, Beth, Jack, Marty.
Narrator:	Beth, Jack and Marty are on holiday staying with their Auntie Michelle and Uncle Troy in Northern Queensland, Australia. The three of them take a picnic down to the beach where they see Uncle Troy's small boat, or 'tinny' as it is called, locally, and Jack suggests they go for a sail, against Beth's better judgement. Now, someway out from shore, Beth is getting worried.
Beth:	'This is far enough, Jack. Uncle Troy said he'd take us out to one of the islands in their motor boat another day. We don't know anything about the currents around here or the weather'.
Jack:	*(rowing the boat)* 'But it's so calm. Look. Like a mirror. No problem'.
Marty:	'I think we should go back, too. This is the sea in Australia, not a lake in England'.
Jack:	*(looking scornful)* 'Yeah? How clever of you, Marty!'
Beth:	'Stop it, Jack. We can't all be brainy like you. Anyway, he's right'.
Narrator:	Jack keeps rowing without changing direction. Soon they're only a short distance away from one of the islands.
Jack:	*(excitedly)* 'Come on, let's explore. I wonder if there are any cassowaries on this island'.
Marty:	'What's a cassowary?'
Jack:	'It's a big, flightless bird. Come on'.
Marty:	'We could pretend we're Columbus, just discovering Australia'.

Jack:	'No, Marty. You mean Captain Cook. He discovered Australia in 1770. You should know that. We went up to Cooktown last weekend!'
Beth:	'This is silly, Jack. The weather might change and we won't be able to get back'.
Narrator:	They land the boat and drag it a little way up the sand.
Jack:	*(pointing to the sky)* 'Look, it's fine, there's no wind. We won't stay long'.
Beth:	'Just a quick look, then'.
Narrator:	Reluctantly, Beth and Marty follow their brother. By the time they've climbed to the top of the small island they're hot and tired so they sit down in the shade of a clump of palm trees for a while. Soon, they all doze off.
Marty:	*(wakes up, straightens his glasses and looks at his watch)* 'Hey! Wake up! It's after four o'clock!'
Narrator:	They all jump up.
Beth:	*(alarmed)* 'Jack, do you realise that we have no water? You know what Auntie Michelle said about drinking a lot. I can't believe I went along with this'.
Narrator:	Nobody spoke as they set off back to where they'd left the boat. As they climb over the sand dunes and look down onto the beach, Jack gasps.
Jack:	'The boat's gone!'
Marty:	'I don't think it was here that we left it'.
Jack:	'Yes it was. I remember that clump of rocks, and look, this is the nearest point to the mainland. It was definitely here'.
Marty:	*(shaking his head)* 'It doesn't look the same. It wasn't here we left it'.
Jack:	'Shut up, Marty! It was here, only we didn't think of the tide. We should have dragged the boat higher up the beach. It's gone. It's been swept away'.

Narrator:	All three are silent for a moment as the realisation of their situation sinks in.
Marty:	'This is really stupid, Jack! We're marooned here and it's all your fault!'
Jack:	'Don't call me stupid! It's not my fault! You can't blame me!'
Beth:	*(calmly)* 'It's no use getting angry, you two. We'll be rescued soon'.
Marty:	*(turning on Beth)* 'How? No-one knows we're here! We weren't supposed to take the boat out in the first place'.
Beth:	'There's no point in panicking, Marty. They'll go and look on the beach and see that the boat's gone. At least we're safe here'.
Jack:	'How will they know which island we're on? There are so many of them. What shall we do?'
Marty:	'We should make a fire. Then someone will see the smoke'.
Jack:	'Oh, very clever! I suppose you just happen to have a box of matches with you?'
Marty:	'You don't need matches, you can start a fire with the sun and a piece of glass'.
Narrator:	Jack opens his mouth to make a retort but Marty takes off his glasses. Then he gathers some dry grass into a pile.
Beth:	'Don't you think you ought to build the fire on the beach? Then you won't set fire to the whole island'.
Narrator:	Marty picks up his heap of dry grass and moves it onto the sand. Kneeling down, he holds one of the lenses of his glasses over it so that the sun's rays are focussed into a point. Soon a wisp of smoke drifts from the grass and he blows on it, gently, until a flame appears.
Marty:	'Get some leaves! Quick! They'll make better smoke'.
Narrator:	The fire is soon burning well but there is no sign of rescue.
Jack:	*(picks up a handful of sand and flings it into the water, angrily)*

	'When is someone going to come for us? We might be here all night!'
Beth:	'We'll be OK, Jack'.
Marty:	*(face brightens as idea comes to him)* 'Hey Jack! Why don't you swim to the shore and get help? You can easily swim that far'.
Jack:	'Oh, a great idea! There might be sharks out there. Anyway, it's always further than it looks across water'.
Beth:	'We should stick together. We're all right and it won't be dark for hours'.
Narrator:	Marty suddenly jumps up and goes off towards the few scattered trees. Then he starts looking around on the ground as if searching for something. At last, he picks up a thick stick, walks back to the beach and writes SOS in the sand in giant letters.
Marty:	'In case they send out a helicopter looking for us'.
Beth:	'Good thinking, Marty'.
Jack:	'I'm really thirsty. We were idiots not to bring any water'.
Marty:	*(feeding more leaves onto the fire)* 'We could distil some sea water and make a fishing line and catch a fish and cook it on the fire'.
Beth:	*(looks up at Marty and grins)* 'Have you been reading 'Robinson Crusoe' or something?'
Jack:	'We're not planning on being here that long, Marty. Have you thought of the trouble we'll be in when we get back? Especially if they have to call out the Air/Sea Rescue or something. Typical stupid tourists, they'll say'.
Marty:	'We'll be famous!'
Beth:	'That's hardly the word I'd use. It'll be really embarrassing'.
Jack:	'I'm sorry. It was my idea to take the boat and it was really stupid'.
Marty:	'You said it, and you're supposed to be the brains of the family'.

Narrator:	It's still very warm and there is no wind. Smoke from the fire drifts straight up. Beth is gazing out over the water. Suddenly she jumps to her feet.
Beth:	'There's a boat! Look!'
Marty:	'Wave! Take off your shirts or hats and wave them. I'll put more stuff on the fire to make it blaze up'.
Narrator:	The boat comes closer. The three children jump up and down, shouting and waving.
Marty:	'It's their motor boat! Uncle Troy's and Auntie Michelle's! I knew they would come'.
Narrator:	There are hugs and tears of relief and nobody gets into trouble. Marty is praised for his fire, which is what led to their rescue.

End

Questions

1. Was Jack very knowledgeable? What makes you say so?

2. Was Marty very knowledgeable? What evidence is there for this?

3. Was Beth very knowledgeable? In what way?

4. Who made good use of their knowledge and what is your evidence?

5. Are there some kinds of knowledge that are more easily made practical than others or can all knowledge be useful?

6. Does knowledge have to have a use? Why? Why not?

7. Which person was the best at creative thinking? What is the evidence to support your opinion?

Thought for the Day:

If we only have knowledge to show off or get people to think how clever we are, it is wasted. It is more intelligent to be able to use your knowledge to meet the need of each moment. That may be in school work, or it may be in any situation in which we find ourselves.

How often do we think we know about something, only to find we only had partial knowledge? Trouble arises when we have made decisions based on our partial knowledge. This traditional story from India illustrates this in a humorous way.

The Blind Men and the Elephant

Long ago, in India, there lived six men who had all been blind since birth. Often they would meet and sit in the shade of a tree to talk about their experiences and one day the subject of discussion was the elephant. None of them knew what it looked like, of course, but they had heard many stories of this great beast.

One day, they heard that a rich man who owned an elephant was to visit a nearby village so they travelled there and asked him if they could each investigate the elephant. The rich man was happy to show off his possession and led the first blind man up to the great beast.

The first man tripped over a rock and fell against the elephant's side, putting out his hands to save himself. He felt the thick rough skin as far as he could reach.

'Oh', he said, 'it's like a great wall'.

The second man went forward, his hands outstretched. The elephant had turned slightly and the first thing the man touched was its tusks.

'It's long and hard and smooth', he said, 'just like a spear'.

The third man stepped towards the elephant, a little to the rear, and grabbed its tail.

'No', he said. 'It's coarse and pliable like a thick rope'.

It was the turn of the fourth man.

He reached out and touched the trunk.

'It is long and squirms and wriggles like a snake', he said, as the elephant wrapped it around his waist.

Then came the fifth man, who touched the animal's ear.

'No', he muttered, in awe. 'I feel one of its wings here. It is a flying animal'.

Finally, the sixth man stepped forward, intrigued by what his friends had said. Now, at last, he would know for himself. He touched one of the legs. He felt it up and down and side to side.

'You are all wrong', he said. 'It is like the trunk of a stout, palm tree'.

The six blind men went back to the shade of their tree to discuss - and argue - about their experiences. All thought they were right, since they had felt the elephant for themselves.

All were partly right - yet all were wrong.

End

Questions

1. Why do you think this story is told? What is the lesson that can be learned from it? *(Full knowledge of something is better than partial knowledge).*

2. At the start, the men didn't have any knowledge about an elephant. How did they begin to get some knowledge? How do we get knowledge of something?

3. Each of the men had a little knowledge about an elephant. Why is it important to have as much knowledge of a situation as possible?

4. Can we always rely on the knowledge we have of something? Can you think of any occasions when we couldn't rely on information?

5. Often, we get knowledge of something, and we make decisions based on that. For example, someone tells us that the bus leaves at ten past one, so we make sure we get to the bus-stop before ten past one. What happens to our decision making when we only have partial knowledge of something? *(We make poor decisions).*

Thought for the Day:

It is easy to get ourselves into trouble when we make decisions based on partial knowledge. Try to have as much knowledge of a situation as possible before making decisions.

This old story from the Zen tradition in Japan shows a subtle notion in quite a simple way. We are full of ideas, habits, likes and dislikes, all of which have been taken on at sometime in life - probably without consciously knowing at the time what was happening. If we really want to know about something we have to set aside all the inbuilt prejudices and try to see it as if for the first time.

Nan-In and the Professor

A long time ago in Japan there lived a man called Nan-In. He lived during the Meija era, which was from 1868 to 1912. Nan-In was a follower of the Zen Buddhist religion and was admired by many people in his village for his wisdom and understanding. If people had a problem they would go to see Nan-In to seek his counsel and get his advice. In his answers to people, Nan-In would try to put into practice what he had learned from hours of studying the Buddhist scriptures.

Whether it was a quarrel between neighbours, or worries about the harvest, Nan-In would think carefully about the problem and sit still and quiet to see what thoughts came to mind. He would always try to be fair, as well as practical, in his answers.

Nan-In did not seek fame, but over the years, as he dealt wisely with more and more people, his wisdom began to spread. At last the stories of Nan-In's wisdom reached the ears of a learned professor in a distant city. The stories began to make the professor curious. How could a poor monk have such a reputation for wisdom, he wondered? After all, the monk had not gone to university as he himself had. The professor determined to visit the monk to find out about his wisdom and ask him to explain about Zen.

Now, in those days, it wasn't such an easy task to travel over long distances. You couldn't just get on a train or 'plane, or drive yourself there in a car. The professor made all the preparations for his long journey. He told his friends not to expect to see him for at least a month, because he was going on a long journey to see a monk called Nan-In and ask him about Zen.

At last, it was time to leave, and the professor got on the horse he had borrowed, and set off. He knew the general direction, but as he didn't have a map he asked about Nan-In as he went. He would ask people if they had heard of him and knew where he was to be found.

At last, after nearly two weeks travelling, a tired and sore professor walked into the village of Haikusan where Nan-In lived, leading his horse behind him. He found an inn where he could stay for the night and went to bed early, planning to visit Nan-In next morning.

As usual, Nan-In was up very early the next morning. After washing and meditating, he spent some time studying a piece of scripture he had been puzzling over. Then he started to do his daily chore of gathering wood for the fire. As he was doing this he saw a man approaching him. He knew he was a visitor to the village, and stood up to greet him.

The professor introduced himself to Nan-In and told him that he had travelled a long way to meet him and to ask about Zen. Being a proud and vain person he spent a long time telling Nan-In about how important he was in the city in which he lived, and how he had studied for many years.

Nan-In listened politely and asked his visitor if he would like tea. He led the way into his small house and began to prepare the tea. Nan-In carried the teapot to the professor's cup and began to pour the tea. The cup was soon full, but Nan-In just kept on pouring. The professor watched in amazement as it overflowed. At last he could contain himself no longer.

'The cup is full, no more will go in', he said.

'Like this cup', said Nan-In, 'you are full of your own ideas and opinions. How can I show you Zen if you don't first empty your cup?'

End

Questions

1. The professor was described as a proud and vain person. How would you describe Nan-In?

2. What did Nan-In mean when he said that the professor was full of his own ideas and opinions?

3. Why did it matter? What difference did it make?

4. What did Nan-In mean when he told the professor he must 'first empty his cup'?

5. Why did Nan-In keep on pouring the tea until it over-flowed, why didn't he just tell the professor he thought he was too full of old ideas?

6. What does it mean when we say 'keep an open mind'? Do you think this is important? Why?

Thought for the Day:

Sometimes we can be so full of our old ideas that we don't open up to new ones. We can all learn from each other - we all have worthwhile things to share.

'A little learning is a dangerous thing', is an old saying. Perhaps a corollary would be, 'A little knowledge is a dangerous thing', especially when it is acted upon. This little play is a light-hearted look at the problem of knowing a little and making up the rest.

Little Red Riding Hood's Basket

Cast: Narrator, Little Red Riding Hood, Nicole, Jason, Max, Heather, Teacher.

Narrator: You all know the story of Little Red Riding Hood, don't you? But what do you think happened after she and her grandmother were saved from the wolf by the huntsman?

She was late for school, of course. And she got into trouble, partly because she was late and partly because she said the wolf had taken the basket and her homework had been in it.

Do you think your teacher would believe you if you said that you were just taking some soup and cake to your Gran, who wasn't well, when a wolf ate her up and then pretended to be her . . . ? Well, you know the story.

Of course they wouldn't. And Red Riding Hood's teacher didn't believe her, either. It was just an excuse because she hadn't done her homework and it wouldn't be the first time, either.

So she asked if anyone else in the class had seen Red Riding Hood and could back up her story.

Nicole: 'I saw her at the edge of the woods. She was picking flowers and didn't have anything else in her hands. I didn't see a basket or a wolf. She's always talking about wolves, though. Always trying to scare us when we play in the woods. My Dad doesn't believe there are any wolves there any more'.

Jason: 'It's not fair that wolves have such a bad name. They shouldn't be blamed for everything. They're beautiful animals. I'd like one for a pet but my Mum says two dogs are enough. Anyway, wolves don't eat people or cake'.

Max: 'I go past Red Riding Hood's Gran's cottage on my way to school.

114

	I did notice that the door was open this morning so I peeped in to see if she was all right.
Teacher:	'Did you see them there, Max?'
Max:	'Yes. Red Riding Hood was talking to her Gran, who was lying in bed'.
Teacher:	'You didn't see any wolf?'
Max:	'No. Only her Gran sitting up in bed. She looked different though, but I expect that was because she wasn't well. Her ears looked bigger than usual and her nose was long and she was very . . .
Teacher:	'Very what?'
Max:	'Hairy'.
Narrator:	The class giggles.
Teacher:	'Max! You mustn't be rude and make personal remarks about people!'
Max:	'I think she had some new, false teeth, too. They didn't fit properly and were sticking out of the side of her mouth'.
Red Riding Hood:	'That wasn't my Gran, that was the wolf'.
Teacher:	'Do you think it was the wolf, Max?'
Max:	*(shaking his head)* 'Of course not. It must have been her Gran. She had a nightdress and glasses on and was in her Gran's bed. I didn't see a basket though'.
Teacher:	'Did anyone else see Red Riding Hood this morning?'
Heather:	'I did. And she made me really cross. Only yesterday she signed my petition about not killing animals for their skins and then I see her talking to someone wearing a brown fur! What a hypocrite! She seemed friendly with the person, too'.
Teacher:	'Was she carrying a basket?'

Heather: 'Oh, I didn't see one. I was just so mad. Last night I went all round the village getting signatures for the petition AND I did my homework and then I saw that person! In summer too! They must have worn that fur on purpose just to annoy me'.

Teacher: 'Well, Red Riding Hood, no-one saw either your basket or the wolf. I think you've just been telling a fairy story. Make sure you do your homework tonight!'

End

Questions

1. Was it fair of the teacher to question the class to see if Red Riding Hood's story was true? What are the reasons for your answer?

2. Jason talked about wolves having a bad name. Was this anything to do with the teacher's question? Why did he say it?

3. Max thought granny looked a bit strange, with a long, hairy nose, and protruding teeth. Why didn't he think it was a wolf?

4. Can our senses deceive us? If you think so, can you think of an example?

5. Heather didn't see if Red Riding Hood had a basket or not. Why didn't she notice? *(Re-read the sentence if necessary)*.

6. Can your emotions *(feelings)* affect the use of your senses? Can you think of any examples?

Thought for the Day:

Don't make judgements when you only have a little knowledge. Try to be awake, in the present, and use your senses to get as much information as possible of a situation.

Knowledge can be power. We all know the feeling when the ego grows when we know something that others do not know. We gain power, authority, 'kudos', through being able to tell others; or keeping it from them but making it plain that we know! The Sphinx was no exception - she wielded power through knowledge.

The Riddle of the Sphinx
(A Greek Myth)

Sphinxes, as we all know, are creatures with the body of a lion and the head and shoulders of a woman. They occur in old folk tales and myths of many countries and all seemed to have acted as guardians of some sort, though they were not always good.

The sphinx at the entrance to the great city of Thebes was definitely NOT good. In fact, she was evil. She crouched on top of a rock and stopped all travellers who wanted to pass by into the city. Before anyone could pass, they had to correctly answer a riddle. If they got it wrong, the sphinx would kill them and eat them.

Well, no-one could get the riddle right and the people of the city were very angry and afraid. If only someone had this small but vital piece of knowledge, they could be freed from the tyranny of the sphinx forever.

One day, a young man called Oedipus came along and was challenged, as usual, by the Sphinx.

'Ask me your riddle, then', he said, boldly.

The sphinx smiled, smugly, at the arrogant man. 'Tell me then', she said, 'what creature has four feet in the morning, two feet at noon and three feet in the evening?'

Oedipus thought for a moment. Then he said, 'Man. He crawls on all fours as a baby, walks on two legs as a grown man and then has a stick to help him in his old age'.

The smile vanished from the sphinx's face. The answer was correct.

Oedipus passed by, safely, into the city to the cheering of the people and was made King.

The sphinx crept away and died.

End

Questions

1. Do you like knowing something others do not know? Can anyone think of an example when they have liked having some information that others did not have?

2. Why is it that we sometimes like having knowledge that others do not have?

3. Do you think knowledge is useful when it is kept 'contained', or kept to yourself? Why? Why not?

4. The people of Thebes were afraid because they were always asked a riddle - with the possibility of being eaten if they failed to answer it! How do you feel if someone keeps something from you? Why do you think they might do this?

5. Why do you think the Sphinx crept away and died when Oedipus correctly answered the riddle?

6. How do you feel when you share knowledge with someone else?

Thought for the Day:

Knowledge is for sharing. When we keep it to ourselves for selfish reasons it makes us all worse off, but when it is shared it benefits everyone.

Wisdom

Children *(and adults)*, often have the idea that to be wise one has to be old - that wisdom is in effect an accumulation of knowledge. Perhaps, however, wisdom is related to the use of knowledge - which makes us all potentially wise, children and all. Being learned is different to being wise.

The Shorter Oxford Dictionary lists wise as being 'the capacity for judging rightly in matters relating to life and conduct'. Aristotle says that one can be wise about 'this or that'. He cites examples of a doctor being wise in relation to the actions he takes as regards the health of his patients, or a harbour pilot being wise with regard to actions that bring a ship, safely, to berth. In ways such as these all of us can be wise, but this, he says, is different to being a wise person. The wise person then, is not only wise in matters of particular expertise, but 'in matters relating to life and conduct'. The practical nature of wisdom opens up the possibility for each of us to be wise.

Children readily see and understand the relationship between decisions *(choices)* and consequences, that each day they make hundreds of decisions, each of which has an effect. One boy gave an example, saying that he had been 'hacked' whilst playing football. In a moment of anger he was just about to hit the other player but realised the action had not been malicious and so chose to ignore it and play on. He spoke clearly of the consequences of his action and how these would have been hugely different had he punched the other boy. He considered he had made a wise decision. The best way to grow in wisdom is to practice being wise! The deeper meaning and relevance can be explored through dialogue once children have real examples.

The stories in this section try to engage children in considering wisdom, and in developing their understanding through practical examples.

Knowledge and wisdom are different things. Knowledge in action is wisdom. Lisa has read a lot of books about horses but that is not the same as having the experience to use that knowledge, so she ends up being not very wise.

The Horse's Tail

'I know all about horses', said Lisa, as the two girls walked up the long drive to the stables. 'Did you know that their height is measured in hands and that each hand is four inches - that is ten centimetres?'

Jan had to keep running to catch up with her friend's long strides. She was quite a lot shorter than Lisa.

'They can be quite nervous animals', Lisa went on. 'My mum said that when she used to ride it was always on dustbin day and she often had the horse who was terrified of the truck. It was real scary'.

'You've never ridden before, though, have you?' panted Jan.

Lisa shook her head. 'But I know your shoulders, hips and ankles should all line up', she said. 'And you never kick the horse, you just squeeze with your legs'.

Jan knew a bit about horses, too. She loved reading books about ponies. That's what had given her the idea of having a riding lesson for a birthday present, and bringing a friend along, too.

'Did you see that film called 'The Horse Whisperer'?' asked Lisa. 'Oh, that was a great film'.

'Yes, it was', agreed Jan, although she hadn't seen the film. She'd really wanted to see it when it was at the cinema but now she'd have to wait until it was on TV.

'I wonder what colour my pony will be', Lisa was saying. 'Did you know that there's no such thing as a white or black horse? I know all the colours. There's . . .'

Jan sighed. This was her long awaited birthday present and she was already fed up with Lisa. She could be a real know-all and make everyone else feel like dunces.

As they turned a bend in the track they heard a lot of snorting and whinnying and stomping. Ahead, partly hidden by a large oak tree, a horse was prancing about and rearing up on its hind legs.

'It's gone mad!' said Lisa, running forward. 'Its tail is caught in the fence. Poor thing, it's all in a lather and really panicking'.

The horse was in a state. Its eyes were rolling and it was covered in a creamy sweat. The more it tugged the more firmly its tail became entangled in the fence.

'Daft thing', said Lisa. She reached forward to try and untangle the strands of horse hair.

'Be careful of its hooves!' yelled Jan.

'It's got a halter on', said Lisa. 'I'm going in to see if I can grab its head and calm it down'.

'Don't be silly, Lisa. You're not a horse whisperer. That animal is dangerous'.

'It's going to kick the fence down at this rate', said Lisa. She climbed over, well away from the horse, and then began to approach it, talking softly.

Meanwhile, Jan set off up the track as fast as she could. When she got nearer to the stables she began to shout.

Two stable hands came out. Quickly, Jan explained what was happening and they ran back to the horse, followed more slowly by Jan.

The stable lads, experienced with horses, walked confidently into the field. While one grabbed its halter, the other quickly cut the tail free of the fence. One of them looked at Lisa.

'That was a fool thing going near that horse. One kick could have seriously hurt you. What were you thinking of? Your friend had more sense, coming quickly for expert help'.

Lisa tossed her head. 'I'm not ignorant about horses', she said. 'I was trying to calm him down'.

'Well', said the other lad, 'knowledge is one thing but you have to use your brains, too. And, incidentally, this is a mare'.

End

122

Questions

1. Did Lisa really know a lot about horses? What is your evidence? Did Lisa think she knew a lot about horses?

2. Was it a wise action to go into the field with the horse? Why did Lisa do it?

3. Is knowledge the same as wisdom - if you know a lot about something is that the same as being able to be wise about it?

   Can you think of any examples of this?

4. What was the wise action in the story? Why?

5. Has anyone an example of being able to use knowledge in an action, and so be wise? *(If the concept is too difficult, use the example given in the introduction to 'Wisdom' to stimulate thought).*

Thought for the Day:

   Being wise is making good choices based on knowledge. When we make a good choice a wise action follows it. We heard an example of this that shows there are lots of small ways every day when we can be wise.

None of us wants to be thought stupid, and the Emperor and his subjects were no exceptions. We all sometimes pretend to know or understand things we don't know - but, fortunately, without such embarrassing consequences!

The Emperor's New Clothes

There was nothing the Emperor liked better than clothes, in fact he had a set for every hour of the day. He spent all his money on costumes of the very finest cloth and loved to take part in processions along the streets to show them off to his people.

One day, two weavers arrived in the city proclaiming that they could weave a very special sort of fine cloth which was as light as a spider's web and made of the very best thread to be found in the whole world. The special feature of this material was that it appeared invisible to all incompetent and stupid people and could therefore only be seen by those who were clever and wise.

The Emperor thought that this would be a wonderful way of showing up those of his courtiers who were not fit to hold their jobs so he ordered a suit of clothes to be made from this fine fabric.

The weavers ordered silk and satin and gold thread and demanded a lot of money, which they stashed away. Then they got to work on their empty looms, pretending to weave.

The Emperor became impatient after a while, and although he did not consider himself stupid, he was a little afraid to go himself to see how the weaving was getting on, so he sent his old Minister of Weavers.

There sat the weavers, at their looms, their arms going this way and that, as if they were spinning. The Minister of Weavers could not see anything, because, of course, there was nothing to see, but he did not want to admit it.

'Do you not like this fine cloth?' asked one of the weavers. 'Just look at the colours! Feel the texture'.

'It is exquisite', said the Minister of Weavers. 'The Emperor will be delighted'.

A grand procession was arranged, and, the night before, the weavers stayed up all night so that the clothes would be finished. They cut and sewed in the air and everyone was very impressed with their hard work. The clothes were admired constantly.

124

Finally, it was time for the Emperor to be dressed. He stood in front of the weavers who were holding the invisible clothes up for his inspection. The Emperor, of course, was dismayed that he could see nothing, but he didn't admit it.

'Please remove your clothes, Sire', said one the weavers. The Emperor did so.

Then they pretended to fit his shirt, his trousers and his cloak, doing up buttons here and there *(there were no zips in those days)*. Then they stood back, admiringly.

'Oh, what a good fit, Sire!' said one.

'Wonderful!' said the other. 'The colour suits you admirably'.

The Emperor looked in the mirror, turning this way and that, pretending to admire the clothes.

'All is ready, Sire!' cried one of his chamberlains. The Emperor went outside and the procession began. He strode along, proudly, two chamberlains behind, pretending to carry the train of his cloak.

All the people had heard about this fabulous cloth and they praised the two weavers and admired the clothes.

All that is, except one little girl, who had been away staying with a relative and hadn't heard about the special cloth.

'The Emperor has nothing on!' she shouted.

Her father heard her. 'The innocent voice of a child', he said, and began to tell other people.

Soon the cry went up, 'The Emperor has no clothes on!'

The Emperor knew that they were right but he carried on the procession, his head held high, while his chamberlains still pretended to carry the train that wasn't there.

End

Questions

1. Why did the weavers play this trick on the Emperor and his people?

2. Why was the Emperor taken in by the trick?

3. How do you think the Emperor felt when he couldn't see the cloth?

4. How do you feel when someone calls you stupid or laughs if you don't understand something straight away? Do you think that person knows everything? Is that person wise? Why or why not?

5. The Emperor had a feeling inside that there was no cloth, so why didn't he trust that feeling? Was that wise?

6. The Emperor believed what the weavers said. Do you think you should believe everything that people say? Would that be wise? Why or why not?

Thought for the Day:

The Emperor was so vain it stopped him being wise and seeing the truth about the cloth. If we are not careful, things such as pride, vanity, or trying to show off can get in the way of taking wise actions.

Many children equate wisdom with cleverness. This story seeks to show that one can be clever and wise - or clever and not wise! Wisdom is more about using intelligence to make good decisions than just being 'smart'.

A Day With Year 4

Liam Pemberton sat down and placed his books and pens neatly on the desk in front of him. Across the aisle he noticed Joanne Hunt, arms folded, grinning as she watched Mrs Saunders switch on the computer. What was she up to now? He too watched the monitor as the programmes loaded. Suddenly the teacher stepped back from the computer in alarm. There on the screen for all to see was a large, red and green parrot. The whole class shrieked with laughter. Then the door opened and the Head looked in.

'What's happened to the computers?' he asked. 'Do you think it's a virus? Every time I try to delete it, it screeches horribly'.

Mrs Saunders looked around the class and her eyes rested on Joanne. 'I don't suppose you know anything about this, Joanne?'

Everyone turned to look at her, including Liam. Joanne was really clever at IT, in fact she was clever at a lot of things but how she wasted her talents, Liam thought. He remembered when last term she had done a beautiful bit of graffiti on the school wall and then had to spend all the lunch break washing it off.

Now, Joanne grinned. 'I can easily get rid of it', she said.

Liam watched as she walked up to the computer and began clicking a few keys. She had the attention and admiration of the whole class and Liam couldn't help feeling a little envious.

Meanwhile, Mrs Saunders gave out the Science papers she'd marked.

'Excellent, as usual, Liam', she said, putting his neat essay in front of him. 'You certainly have a good understanding of chemistry'.

At lunchtime the class tumbled out of the classroom and made for the dining area. On the door was a huge and colourful poster which read: *'Have you washed your hands?'* Underneath, was a picture of a pair of hands teaming with germs of all shapes and sizes and all with ghastly faces. In the hands was a sandwich and some of the germs were crawling onto it.

'Is this your work?' Liam asked the boy next to him.

Drew smiled and nodded. 'It's part of my Health and Safety Project for Environmental Studies', he said.

Liam grinned. 'I reckon the kids here will have the cleanest hands in town'.

Drew laughed. 'This isn't the safest school in town though', he said. 'I found eight hazards and Mr Gray is going to make sure something is done about them'.

The two boys went in to lunch. Liam was pleased to be a mate of Drew's as he was always a popular boy, the sort who everyone went to if they had a problem. A sort of agony uncle, Liam thought. Full of good advice.

That afternoon they had French and Liam was asked to conjugate the verb 'to have' which they'd been learning the day before. Liam recited them without hesitation.

'Let's have some role play', suggested Mrs Saunders. 'Can anyone think of a situation?'

'How about a group of kids lost in France ?' said Joanne, and everyone laughed. That very thing had happened during their school trip there last summer and it was Drew who had not only asked directions but also understood the answers. Liam had been with him and remembered how totally useless he'd felt. He knew any amount of verbs and vocabulary but putting them together and making sense was beyond him. For the first time in his life he'd felt really stupid.

At two o'clock the class got out their maths books. Mrs Saunders gave them some quick fire mental arithmetic and in the end had to stop Liam from answering.

'Let's give the others a chance, Liam', she said.

So, he had to sit and watch others working out the sums with calculators hidden under their desks, but he said nothing. Once he'd scoffed at their use but now he knew better. But he did have the satisfaction of knowing that he was faster than any calculator.

At home time, Joanne caught up with him as he unhooked his jacket from the peg.

'Liam', she said, grinning mischievously. 'I know how brilliant you are at chemistry'.

'So?' he said.

'I've got a great idea!'

End

Questions

1. Was Joanne a clever person? What is the evidence?

2. Was Liam a clever person? What is the evidence for that?

3. Who would you say was the wiser person? Why?

4. Liam was very good at saying French verbs so why hadn't he felt very clever when he had been in France the year before?

5. What is it that changes knowledge into wisdom?

6. Can anyone think of a time they have used knowledge in a wise way?

Thought for the Day:

A lot of knowledge will make you clever, but it won't make you wise. To be wise you have to use your knowledge in a way that has good consequences.

Many people seem to associate wisdom with age, that somehow, life experience and wisdom are the same thing. Mark is no exception, but he begins to see that not only can he be wise, but that so can everyone else.

A Little Wisdom

'I can't be wise', said Mark.

'Why not?' asked his teacher, Miss Fletcher.

Mark shrugged. He thought of the times he'd heard about being wise. The three wise men. The wise old owl.

'You have to be old', went on Mark. 'You have to know a lot and have had things happen to you'.

'Well, you're wrong', said the teacher. 'Anyone can be wise. It's all about thinking things out and making the right decisions, based on your experiences. All you children have had experiences in your short lives. You can be wise in small ways'.

Mark wasn't convinced.

When Miss Fletcher had asked the class to find out what wisdom was, Mark was sure it was something he could be when he was older. How could children be wise? That was silly.

The next day, during break, Mark overheard Harry Mason teasing the new boy in their class and challenging him to a fight. Harry Mason was the biggest boy in the class. He had spiky black hair which made him look like Denis the Menace.

'Hey, don't be stupid, Mase', said Mark. 'You're twice his size. Leave him alone'.

Harry turned to Mark. 'Oh, you're going to take his side, are you? Maybe you'd like to fight me in his place?' He towered over Mark, flexing his muscles mockingly.

It wouldn't be the first time Mark had scrapped with Harry but he always came off worst.

'No', he said. 'I'm not fighting you now. Listen, I thought you wanted some new blood in your football team?'

'Yeah. So what?' said Harry.

'I hear this kid was something of a phenomenon at his old school'.

Harry turned to the new boy, his eyebrows raised. 'Is that right? Okay. Come to practice tomorrow after school. Show us what you can do'.

Mrs Kent, the playground assistant, stopped Mark as he wandered back towards his classroom.

'I saw what happened out there, Mark. Very wise of you'.

Mark stared after her. Him, wise? Anyone would be wise not to fight with Harry Mason.

Funny, he thought, that's the second time someone had told him he had done a wise thing recently. He remembered his Dad saying, last week, that he had made a wise decision. That was when he'd got all his homework done on Friday evening so that he had the weekend free. But that was a very small wisdom.

Mark smiled. Surely if he was wise in small things now, he would be wise in bigger things when he was older? It was just a matter of thinking through your actions and seeing their outcome. Of seeing what would be best for all concerned in the end.

Harry Mason was coming towards him, a big grin on his face and his hair like a jagged halo around his head. But he was no angel. He always seemed to be in trouble one way or the other. Perhaps because he wasn't very wise in making decisions. Denis the Menace was right.

He grasped Mark's sweater and half lifted him off the ground.

'Hey Mark. What's so funny?'

'Just the pleasure of seeing you, Mase', said Mark, wisely.

End

Questions

1. Why did Mark think that he couldn't be wise?

2. What did Mark actually say or do to change Harry's mind about fighting? Do you think this was a wise action? Why?

3. Mark thought that if you practised being wise in small things you would learn to be able to be wise in bigger things. Do you think this is true? Have you any evidence?

4. Has anyone an example of being wise? *(Take examples)*

5. *(Addressing one or more who reply)* Why do you think that action was wise? What is there about it that makes it wise?

6. On the evidence we've heard, do you think it is possible for each one of us to be wise?

Thought for the Day:

We can all be wise in our actions by making good choices when we are involved in everyday situations. The only way to do that is by being awake and aware at the time, and realizing what the consequences of our actions will be.

Shandy was in an awkward situation - would he join in with his new friend's shoplifting or threaten the friendship by having nothing to do with it? Should he stick by what he knew to be right? What were the consequences of acting or not acting? This story brings wisdom down to practical realities.

Walking Away

'Hey, Shandy, do you fancy looking around the shops after school?' said Alex.

Shandy looked at his new friend. Alex Baker was confident and bright. Being new at the school, Shandy would have been pleased of any friend, but Alex was popular and well respected. He knew his mum would approve of him too, and would hope some of his self-assurance might rub off.

'Yeah,' he answered. 'Okay'.

Later that afternoon, they drifted along the mall, looking in shop windows, bags slung over their shoulders. Shandy tried to copy Alex's cool swagger.

'Let's go in here', said Alex. 'Easy pickings'.

'Easy what?' said Shandy, but the other boy didn't reply.

They stopped at the mobile phone accessories.

'You got a mobile?' asked Alex.

Shandy nodded. 'In my bag, but it's just for emergencies. Mum doesn't let me use it much'.

Alex made a snorting sound. Then he picked up a leather phone case.

'Look! I like this one, don't you?'

Shandy's eyes lit up. 'Oh yeah! But look at the price. £10.99'.

'They're giving them away today,' said Alex, with a grin, and tucked the packet up the sleeve of his jacket with a quick practised movement of the wrist.

Shandy stared at Alex, then he looked round, but no-one seemed to have noticed.

'One more thing on my shopping list today', said Alex. 'Over here'.

He walked down another aisle but Shandy didn't follow, he just stared after him. He wanted to follow. That would be the easiest thing. Alex was his new mate, his only one, so far. If he didn't go along with this what would happen at school? Would he be an outcast, teased and called names? How he wanted to follow Alex, after all, no-one had seen him steal the phone case.

Alex turned around, a big grin on his face. He beckoned to Shandy.

Shandy tried to grin back and started to walk towards him. Should he overlook it this time, pretend it had never happened but never come shopping with him again? He desperately wanted to be accepted at the new school.

Alex had a packet of batteries in his hand . . .

Shandy decided. He turned and walked out of the shop, past the check-outs with a clear conscience. Then he waited for Alex a little way along the mall, watching the shop exit.

After a couple of minutes Alex walked out. No-one stopped him. No hand reached to apprehend him. No alarm rang.

Alex looked round and spotted Shandy.

'Hey! What's up? Scared were you?' he said, laughing. 'Here. Your phone case'.

Shandy looked down at it. 'No thanks. You keep it. You took the risks'.

Alex shrugged and put it in his pocket. 'Please yourself'. His tone was cool.

All the way out of the mall Shandy expected them to be stopped by a security man. Every time someone looked at them, he was sure they knew. Would he be caught, too, as an accessory? Nervously, he looked over his shoulder.

At last, they were out in the street again and Shandy breathed more easily. He wanted to say something to Alex, to explain.

'It's not right', he began, his heart thumping. 'Taking stuff is not right'.

Alex snorted again. 'They've got more money than we've got', he said. 'Those big shops, they make plenty of profit'.

Shandy said nothing.

Alex grabbed his arm. 'Okay goody-goody, so what are you going to do now, snitch on me?'

Shandy shook his head. 'No, I won't do that', he said. 'I just don't want to be a part of it, okay?'

Soon after, the two boys went their separate ways. Shandy knew that he had lost a friend and hoped it was worth it. He was disappointed and apprehensive about what life would be like at school.

No, his mum would NOT approve of Alex Baker but she would be proud of her own son if she ever knew about what happened today, and he wasn't going to tell anyone.

He would never go shopping with Alex again, but if he happened to see him or anyone else shop-lifting again he would know what he must do.

End

Questions

1. What were the arguments going on in Shandy's mind after he had seen Alex hide the 'phone case in his jacket?

2. Why had those arguments arisen in the first place? *(Shandy knew that what he had seen was against what he knew to be right).*

3. Has anyone ever had a similar decision to make? *(Hear examples. Ask whether the decision was difficult, and why).*

4. What were the consequences of Shandy's actions? What could the consequences have been if he had joined Alex in stealing?

5. How did Shandy feel afterwards?

Thought for the Day:

All our actions have consequences. We can make wise or good decisions which have good consequences, but when we make poor decisions our actions lead to bad consequences. If you stay awake to what is happening by being in the present, it is easier to see choices and make better decisions.

Justice

Justice, according to the dictionary, is righteousness and equity; the quality of being morally just. Being just is being impartial, equitable, fair. Keeping the rule of law is just - obeying the rules. When everyone lives by the law *(rules)* then natural justice is confirmed or realised. When people do not live by the rules of their society injustice is done.

The most important aspect of justice, however, comes from within each individual - being true to that which is known to be right. As Laertes is about to embark for France he is given advice by his father Polonius, 'This above all: to thine own self be true, and it must follow, as the night the day, thou canst not then be false to any man'. *(Hamlet Act 1, Sc. 3).*

Plato also takes this view in Laws IX (864) where it is said, 'But when the opinion of the best . . . has dominion over the soul and orders the life of every man, even if it be sometimes mistaken, yet what is done in accordance therewith and the principle in individuals which obeys this rule, and is best for the whole life of man, is to be called just . . . '

Justice is not something that is done by someone to others. Children should learn, and see in practice in their own lives, that justice comes from within. They may reflect justice in their own conduct, and see it also in the workings of the school - pupil council, mentoring systems, discipline system.

A just society is brought about by having just citizens, not by having external constraints on them.

Justice is linked with compassion and understanding. This story is derived from the well known passage in The Bible: John 8:1-11

The Woman Who Had Done Wrong

The woman crouched in a corner, her back against the cold, stone, wall. Shivering, she pulled the shawl tighter around her shoulders. She shivered with fear as well as with cold. She had committed a crime and had been caught. She knew what her punishment would be. She would be stoned to death.

Anxiously, she watched the doorway, listening for footsteps. It was dawn and the sun's rays crept through the door casting long bright patches onto the stone floor.

Suddenly, the men were there, grabbing her arms and dragging her to her feet. She blinked in the bright sunshine of the courtyard. There were many people there, and one man in front of them. He was the one they called Jesus.

The woman felt a hand in her back pushing her forward. All eyes were on her and she bowed her head.

'Teacher, this woman was caught committing a crime,' said one of the men. 'In the Law, Moses commanded us to stone such women. Now, what do you say?'

Jesus bent down and began writing on the ground with his finger. He had been teaching the people and had been interrupted.

'Did you hear?' asked another, picking up a large rock off the ground. 'This woman has done wrong. She should be stoned'.

Many others began searching for stones and shouting insults at her. Some had even drawn back their arm ready to throw.

The woman cowered, shielding her face with her arms.

Then, Jesus slowly got to his feet and spoke.

'If any one of you is without sin, let him be the first to throw a stone at her'.

The men looked at each other. One by one they lowered their arms. One by one they crept away until there was only Jesus and the woman left. Now she put her arms down and looked at him. He was busy writing on the ground again.

Then he stood up and turned to her. 'Where are they? Has no-one condemned you?'

'No-one, Sir', she said.

'Then neither do I condemn you', said Jesus. 'Go now, and don't do wrong again'.

End

Questions

1. The first response of the people was to condemn the woman. They were shouting about how terrible she was, and wanted to punish her. If someone does something wrong in the classroom or the playground, what is your first response? *(Children may have a variety of responses).*

2. *(To those who have answered)*
   Why have you had that response? *(Encourage the children to look for causes to their actions. Why did they respond like that?)*

3. If you have class or school rules, should there always be the same punishment for breaking them? *(Children should again have reasons for their answers).*
   (This question can stimulate good discussion later, in the classroom).

4. What feeling did Jesus have for the woman?

5. Jesus said, 'If any of you is without sin, let him cast the first stone'. What does this mean?

6. How could this have a meaning for us today?

Thought for the Day:

   Justice is linked to compassion – having feelings for the person who has done something wrong. Remember this, and also that we each of us have faults.

The poem, 'The Bell of Atri', by Henry Wadsworth Longfellow, was inspired by the same legend as this story. Older classes may appreciate being able to read and enjoy the poem after the assembly.

The Bell Of Justice

(An Italian Folk Tale)

The horse shambled up the dusty street. He was old and his coat thin and patchy over his prominent ribs. The day was scorching hot and he looked for shade as well as food.

The streets were deserted. At this time of day, in Italy, it was the custom for people to stay indoors and maybe have a nap, particularly in the heat of summer.

In the market square was a building with overhanging eaves and the horse huddled in the tiny bit of shade it offered. How he longed to be back in the cool stable where he'd lived his whole life. What had he done that his master, the Knight of Atri, should throw him out into the street?

Then he sniffed. There, hanging in front of his nose, was a vine. Not very tasty, but better than nothing. He clamped his teeth round the vine and tugged.

Immediately, a loud clanging rang out, startling the horse. He pulled again at the vine and the noise came again.

Now there were stirrings in the town. People looked out of their windows and opened their doors.

Who was ringing the Bell of Justice?

The Chief of Justice called together his Counsel of judges. No-one had rung the old bell for a long time, though, in the years since King John had hung it there, it had been well used.

The King had declared that anyone who had been wronged was to ring it, and the judges appointed for the purpose would see that justice was done.

Over the years the bell rope had worn through and someone had at last attached a vine to it, which now flourished.

When the Chief of Justice arrived in the square the horse still stood there, a little confused by all the noise and too weak and weary to move. The bell still swung slightly giving the occasion ting.

'That is the Knight of Atri's horse!' exclaimed one of the judges. 'Just look at the poor creature! He's half starved'. And he ordered the horse to be taken to a stable and fed.

'We must summon the Knight to answer for this', said the Chief of Justice.

The Knight was angry at being brought before the counsel. What right had they to question him?

'I can do what I like with my own property', he said. 'That horse was once my best steed but he's old and lazy now, though he eats well enough. I consider it a waste of money to keep a horse which is no longer of any use'. He turned, as if to go, but the Chief of Justice called him back.

'Sire, we are not yet finished. For many years you rode this horse on your campaigns and came back a hero. The town has recognised your chivalry but this act of cruelty does nothing for your reputation. I fear your honour has been replaced by meanness in your lust for gold.'

'This horse served you well without complaint and surely deserves some kindness in his old age. Therefore the law decrees that you provide shelter and food and a pleasant field for him to graze in for the rest of his days'.

The Knight said nothing but mounted his younger horse and galloped away in a swirl of angry dust. His loyal, old horse was led back to his stable.

The Chief of Justice smiled happily. Not only had the bell provided justice for so many people over the years, but now it had even done so for an animal, who neither knew the law nor could speak for itself.

He made a mental note to get the rope repaired.

End

Questions

1. King John had put the bell there so that people could get justice by ringing it, and having their case heard. What do you think justice is?

2. What different ways do we get justice in school?

3. What different ways do we get justice in this country?

4. Is justice the same as revenge? Why or why not?

5. Part of justice is being fairly treated. Do you think that animals should also be fairly treated? Why?

6. The knight thought he could do what he wanted with his property. Is that true here? *(Get children to give reasons for their answers.)*

7. The horse didn't know the law and couldn't speak for itself. Are our laws for some people or for all people? *(i.e. Also those who don't know the law or can't speak up for themselves). Why?*

8. If justice is about fairness and you want to have a just class, or school, or country, how could this best be achieved? *(eg. by having lots of rules or laws, by changing ourselves - how?)*

Thought for the Day:

Justice starts with each of us. Try to treat everyone and everything with fairness. Look for examples of justice during the week.

When terrorist attacks happen, or there is an injustice where innocent people are threatened, quite naturally people are affronted. This story seeks to show that although the rule of law must be maintained, revenge is not part of justice. It takes some strength and wisdom to begin to consider the causes of someone's actions when an horrific act has been perpetrated. Difficult as this is with large events, the same principle can be applied to the everyday occurrences in which we are all involved.

Hostage
(A True Story)

In Holland, in 1977, some children were taken hostage in a school. Four terrorists from the Indonesian Island of South Molucca took the children hostage. At the same time, not far away, others from the same group had hijacked a train and kept over fifty people hostage for twenty days.

Imagine how frightened the hostages must have been all that time, especially the children.

Imagine how frightened their family and friends must have been, and how helpless. There seemed nothing they could do but wait.

Hijackers and kidnappers always want something in return for freeing their victims, but to give in to them would mean that they had won and others would see it as an easy way of getting their way.

Several members of the community wrote to a common friend asking what they could do. This friend was one of those people who others always turn to for advice. Someone who was calm and clear-thinking and wise.

'There is nothing practical we can do', said the friend, 'but we can meditate and pray that the situation will be peacefully resolved. But we must pray for both sides - the captives and the captors. Both need help'.

This may seem strange advice since we usually want the hostages freed. Then it is easy to feel hatred towards the captors and want revenge. To have a peaceful resolution in a conflict, perhaps we must look at both sides of the question and consider the causes. This does not, in any way, mean that the law should not be upheld or the hijackers punished.

The friends carried out the advice but unfortunately the situation did not end entirely peacefully. After twenty days the Dutch Marines stormed the train.

Six of the terrorists and two of the hostages were killed. The 53 remaining passengers were freed, unharmed.

After this, the four terrorists holding the children in the school gave themselves up and the children went home to their families.

End

Questions

1. When something terrible happens, such as the hijacking of a plane or the planting of a bomb, what is our response? What do we feel? Why do we feel like this?

2. Because we care for others, we don't like horrible things to be done to others or to ourselves. Should we have any care for the people who carry out these actions? Why? Why not?

3. What is revenge? Why do people sometimes think of revenge?

4. What is justice? Is revenge anything to do with justice?

5. If someone in the classroom or at home does something wrong do you ever feel sorry for them or have any feelings for them? *(Call for examples and reasons).*

6. Have you ever noticed the reason why someone did something wrong? Did it make a difference to how you felt about the person or how you thought they should be treated?

Thought for the Day:

If someone does something to you that you think is not right (is unjust), look to see what your response is. Is it revenge or justice that you are interested in? Try to put fairness into practice, and be just.

Children often want to know why we have rules and laws. Jessica was no exception, so she asked her Dad about it. Later, as her 'gang' began to break up, she saw in practice why rules are in everyone's interest.

Keeping to The Rules

'Dad', said Jessica. 'Alex says it's against the law to let your dog roam around outside your property'.

'That's right', said Dad. 'Dogs must be under control at all times'.

'That's silly', said Jessica. 'Cats can roam around where they like'.

'Yes, well', said Dad. 'There are different laws for dogs and for cats'.

'That's not fair', said Jessica. 'Why do we have to have silly laws at all?'

'Laws are made for everyone's benefit', answered Dad. 'Without laws in our society there would be anarchy. Everyone would just do whatever they wanted. Do you think that would be a good thing?'

Jessica shrugged. 'I suppose not'.

'Take your question about dogs', went on Dad. 'If you let dogs roam the streets they would breed and maybe form packs which would become wild and attack people. They would be a hazard to traffic too and spread disease. Cats, on the other hand, are loners. They are clean and generally don't hurt people'.

'And they're good climbers', said Jessica. 'It would be hard to keep them in'.

Jessica had four friends at school and they always went around together, in fact, everyone called them 'The Gang'. One day, they had the idea of actually becoming a gang and meeting after school to chat.

'We can use our old summer house for a den', said Jessica.

'And we should have badges and make some rules', said Vicky.

That afternoon, they had their first meeting and decided to meet once a week.

Jessica had taken a notebook. 'Rules', she said, sucking the end of the pen and looking at the others for inspiration.

At the end of the meeting they had five rules.

1. *Bring something to eat to share round.*
2. *Badges must be worn.*
3. *Be punctual.*
4. *Know the password.*
5. *Never tell anyone the password or the location of the den.*

It was fun having a secret gang. They talked and laughed and chewed sweets or ate crisps and sometimes Jessica's Mum would bring them a special treat.

But, one day, Rachel didn't bring anything to eat saying that she'd been hungry and eaten it on the way. They still shared theirs with her as it seemed wrong to leave her out.

The next week she was half an hour late so they waited and when she arrived she did not have her badge on, nor could she remember the password.

'Rachel,' said Vicky. 'Do you want to belong to this gang or not?'

'Yeah, course', said Rachel.

But, the next week, when they were all having a good laugh about something Alex had said to Jessica, there was a sudden shout and two grinning faces looked in at them.

It was two boys from their class.

'The giggle gang', said one. 'That's what you are. We know the password, too'.

The girls looked round at each other. Rachel blushed.

'You've broken all of the rules, Rachel!' said Jessica, crossly. 'It's ruined now'.

Later, that evening, she told her Mum and Dad about their little gang breaking up.

'Why is that?' asked Dad.

'Because Rachel told two boys in our class all about it. In fact, she broke all the rules we'd made'.

'Do you remember asking me about why we have laws?' asked Dad.

Jessica nodded.

'Well, rules are like small laws, aren't they? You can see now, that if everyone obeys the rules or laws, things work well, there is no unfairness or injustice, but, if people don't obey them, it affects everyone'.

Jessica sighed. 'Maybe we can start again, and if Rachel wants to join she'll have to promise to keep to the rules'.

End

Questions

1. What reason did Jessica's Dad give for having rules or laws?

2. Why do you have rules in your classroom or school?

3. What would school be like if there were no rules? Who would suffer?

4. What would our country be like if there were no laws?

5. How do you think Justice is linked to keeping rules or laws? *(Keeping to the law ensures fairness for everybody. Fairness for everybody is justice)*.

6. Jessica's gang broke up because someone couldn't keep to the rules. Have you ever been in a group that broke up because someone couldn't follow the rules? *(Take examples)*.

Thought for the Day:

When we have good laws, keeping to them is fair to everyone and therefore everyone is happy. When some people do not keep the laws (rules), someone always suffers and is made miserable.

We can make this a better and happier school for everyone through everyone trying to keep to the rules.

That's not fair!' How often do we hear children saying or whining that? Fairness is the basis of Justice, and is especially close to the hearts of children. It is important that things are fair, that children are treated fairly, and that they see that things are fair. 'That's not fair', can however become an habitual response when things don't suit the child, and in that circumstance, have nothing to do with fairness. It is important that children do examine issues objectively to see if they really are fair or not.

It's Not Fair!

'It's not fair!' said Maddy, between bites of her sandwich. 'Mum and Dad are going to Paris without us'.

'Well, that's a fine thing', said her Uncle Ted, with a grin. 'And we thought you liked staying with us'.

'Oh, we do', said Maddy. 'But we've never been to Paris, and we could have gone to Disneyland. Do you think Mum and Dad will go there?'

Uncle Ted shook his head. 'There are plenty of other things to see in Paris', he said.

After lunch the four of them went to the beach. Maddy, her brother Joe, Uncle Ted and Auntie Barbara. Not forgetting Jess, their Labrador.

'Let's walk along as far as the pier and back', said Auntie Barbara. 'See you later, Jess'. She locked the car door, making sure one window was left open.

'Why can't Jess come, too?' asked Joe.

'Dogs are not allowed on this part of the beach', said Auntie Barbara.

'That's not fair!' said Joe.

On the pier was a stall selling candy floss and Uncle Ted bought some for each of the children. 'Special treat', he said.

That evening, the children were tired from their journey and the long walk. At eight o'clock Auntie Barbara said, 'I think it's time you both went to bed'.

As they went upstairs, Maddy yawned and said, 'it's not fair! I usually stay up later than Joe because I'm older'.

149

'Look at you, you're tired', said Auntie Barbara. 'Have a good sleep and we'll have another nice day tomorrow'.

Maddy was awoken by Jess licking her face. She giggled and got out of bed, her arm around the dog's neck.

'All right, Jess, I'm up'. She looked out of the window and her face fell as she saw the grey clouds and the misty rain falling.

'It's raining!' she complained to Auntie Barbara, sitting at the table and reaching for her glass of orange juice. 'What can we do today?'

Joe was already there. 'We're going to play a game', he said, through a mouthful of rice crispies.

'What sort of game?' asked Maddy.

'The weather's going to clear up this afternoon', said Auntie Barbara, stacking the dishes in the dishwasher. 'But I thought we'd play a little game. It's called *Justice*'.

Both children looked at her. They'd never heard of that game.

'Yesterday', went on Auntie Barbara, 'you both said that things weren't fair. In fact, three times you said, 'it's not fair!' as children so often do'.

They giggled at her imitation of them.

'What is fairness?' she asked.

'Being the same for everyone', said Joe.

'Justice', said Matty. 'The name of the game. Not giving someone more than another'.

'Yes', said their aunt. 'But there's more to it than that. You have to take into account the circumstances as well. You have to look at every aspect. Let's talk about the things you thought were unfair, yesterday.

'Maddy, you said it wasn't fair that your Mum and Dad went to Paris without you, but it's their Wedding Anniversary, isn't it? Although they love being with you two, don't you think it's nice for them to be together, sometimes? After all, you are having a holiday too'.

Maddy nodded.

150

'Then you, Joe', said their aunt, 'thought it wasn't fair that we couldn't take Jess on the beach. The thing is that not all dogs are well trained by their owners to do their business in the right place. People lie on the beach and children play there, too. Dog dirt can spread diseases. There is a part of the beach further away from the town where dogs can go. So that sounds fair, doesn't it?'

Joe nodded.

'Now, let's look at what wouldn't have been fair', said Auntie Barbara. 'What if someone said that, as a special favour, Jess could go on the beach but other dogs couldn't. That wouldn't be fair. What if Uncle Ted had bought one of you a candy floss and not the other. That wouldn't have been fair, would it?'

'No!' they said, together.

'But', said Auntie Barbara, 'you were right, Maddy, when you said that it wasn't fair you going to bed at the same time as Joe. Being older does give you certain privileges and that is perfectly fair because Joe will get them when he is older'.

Joe pouted but nodded his head at the same time.

'So, next time you say, 'it's not fair!' play the 'Justice' game. Ask yourself if you are just thinking only from your own point of view or if it is reasonable for everyone'.

'Look! It's stopped raining', exclaimed Joe.

Auntie Barbara smiled. 'Fair weather', she said, 'just as they'd forecast'.

End

151

Questions

1. Fairness has to do with Justice. We all like things to be fair. Think of the things that Maddy and Joe thought were not fair. Why did they say they weren't fair?

2. When Aunty Barbara made them think about and examine the things they thought were unfair, the children changed their minds. *(Remind children of the issues that were thought unfair).* Why did they change their minds?

3. Had the events themselves changed? *(The events previously thought unfair).* What had changed? *(Their point of view).*

4. Why had they changed their point of view?

5. If you want to try to be fair to people, and to see if things are really fair, what must you do? *(Be awake to all the circumstances around what it is you are examining. Have as much information as possible).*

Thought for the Day:

Next time you hear yourself saying (or about to say) 'It's not fair!', play the 'Justice' game and think about all the circumstances around your problem. Check if you're only considering yourself. Do you have all the information? Ask yourself – 'Is it really fair?'

Myself

'Know Thyself'. These words are carved over the entrance to the temple at Delphi. They are the basic tenet of Socratic thought and for some, the active search to find the meaning of this injunction forms the purpose of life. On a level more within the experience of most of us, self-knowledge is related to emotional intelligence and this is of huge importance to all of us, children included. Childhood is where the foundations of emotional literacy are laid - where they *must* be laid! In the 'Apology', Socrates says, 'The unexamined life is not worth living'. The stories within this theme are to stimulate children to begin to engage with this difficult concept. Further dialogue in class after assembly would pay great dividends.

As one grows in self-knowledge, that knowledge can be put into effective use in everyday situations - and that surely is emotional intelligence!

Sonnet 53

What is your substance, whereof are you made,
That millions of strange shadows on you tend?
Since every one hath, every one, one shade,
And you, but one, can every shadow lend.
Describe Adonis, and the counterfeit
Is poorly imitated after you;
On Helen's cheek all art of beauty set,
And you in Grecian tires are painted new.
Speak of the spring and the foison of the year:
The one doth shadow of your beauty show,
The other as your bounty doth appear,
And you in every blessed shape we know.
In all external grace you have some part,
But you like none, none you, for constant heart.

William Shakespeare

This story for younger children, shows that we all want to be something other than what or who we are. Sid the snail is no exception, but after a dangerous journey he finds it's always better to be oneself.

The Rainbow Snail

Simon Snail stood proudly in the doorway while his friend Sid gazed, in awe, at his shell.

'It's lovely', said Sid.

Simon looked very pleased and proud. 'The wizard did it', he said.

'It starts with red', said Sid, 'then orange and yellow and green and blue'. He stopped.

'That purple colour is indigo', said Simon.

'Indigo, violet', said Sid. 'It's a rainbow!'

Simon nodded. 'Well, I must be off', he said. 'I want to show my beautiful shell to everyone'.

Sid looked round at his own dull, brown shell. How nice it would be to have a rainbow shell. He would go and ask the wizard to do one for him.

He left his rockery home and went down to the path.

The wizard's house was across the path and past the pond. Everyone knew it was dangerous to cross the path in daytime. But Sid didn't have time to go around the edge. He wanted his new shell NOW. He left the cool shade of his rockery home and went into the bright sunshine. The path felt hot under his foot.

Suddenly, when he was nearly across, there was a thundering sound. Then a hot wind blew on him. Sid looked up.

There, stood a huge, brown, furry monster. Its eyes were as big as he was and they were looking at him. A great, floppy, pink tongue waved above him. Sid was very frightened. More frightened than he had ever been before.

Sid quickly curled right into his shell. He felt the tongue begin to roll him over and over until he came to rest in something soft.

After a long time he peeped out of his shell. He waited. Nothing happened. The monster had gone and he was in the grass.

'Are you all right?' asked a voice, above him.

Sid looked up and saw a pretty orange and yellow butterfly. She landed on a dandelion, her wings still fluttering gently.

'I saw what happened', she said. 'It's dangerous to cross the path in the daytime'.

'I know', said Sid. He looked at her beautiful wings. The bright colours dazzled him. 'But I'm going to ask the wizard to give me a rainbow shell'.

'A rainbow shell?' said the butterfly, in surprise. 'But your colour is just right for you'.

Silly butterfly, thought Sid. It's all right for her to say that. She has pretty, colourful wings.

Sid went on again, through the flower bed and past the pond. A big, green frog was sitting on a lily pad in the middle of the pond.

'I'm going to the wizard to get a rainbow shell', said Sid. 'Why don't you come, too?'

'No, thank you', replied the frog. 'This colour is just right for me'. And he jumped into the water.

Silly frog, thought Sid. Who wants to be that awful, greenish brown?

At last, he reached the wizard's house and knocked on the door.

The wizard opened it and smiled. 'Hello, young Sid', he said. 'What can I do for you?'

'I would like a rainbow shell, like Simon's, please', said Sid, politely.

'I see', said the wizard. 'But, don't you think the colour you have is just right for you?'

'That's what the butterfly said, but she has beautiful coloured wings'.

'Yes', said the wizard. 'That's because butterflies are always amongst flowers.

You see, their wings are coloured like flowers so that they can't be seen'.

Sid went inside the wizard's house.

'The silly frog was happy with his brownish-green colour', said Sid.

'The frog is green like the water plants he sits on', said the wizard. 'All creatures have enemies so they must match the place they live in so that they can't be easily seen'.

Sid looked up at the wise old wizard. 'You gave Simon a rainbow shell', he said.

'Simon is a vain snail', said the wizard, shaking his grey head. 'He wouldn't listen to me.'

'Don't worry. The spell only lasts until sunset. By the time you get back he will be dull brown again, just like the stones and earth where he lives'.

Sid was disappointed and he turned to leave.

The wizard chuckled. 'But your rainbow shell will last much longer than Simon's'.

Sid stopped. What did he mean? He turned his eyes to look at his shell and couldn't believe what he saw.

A RED rose petal was stuck to one side.

An ORANGE dandelion was on the other.

A YELLOW buttercup petal was there too.

And a GREEN blade of grass.

Right in the middle was a BLUE tit's feather.

Further back was . . . an . . . INDIGO pansy petal.

And next to it was a VIOLET petal.

It looked magnificent!

'There. You see', smiled the wizard. 'The dog's lick made your shell sticky. You have a rainbow shell after all AND it will match where you go - so long as you don't cross the path'.

End

Questions

1. Why do you think Sid first wanted a rainbow shell?

2. Why do you think Sid's brown shell was just right for him?

3. What do you think would have happened to him if he had a rainbow shell like Simon's all the time?

4. What do you think the wizard meant by saying, *(about Sid's shell)* 'It will match wherever you go'?

5. Do you sometimes want to be different to the way you are? In what ways do you want to change?

6. Is developing your talents different from wanting to be someone else?

Thought for the Day:

Think about what you are good at and what you like doing. How can you develop and get better at these things?

Who or what am I? Mrs Cook used her apple to demonstrate that it is not an easy question. How many parts or attributes can be taken away and 'apple' still remain? What about with a human being? Whilst being a very difficult question, it is often surprising what children will make of such questions. Thinking about the question is more important than reaching an immediate firm answer.

The Apple

One morning, Mrs Cook brought an apple into the classroom and put it on her desk. No-one thought anything of it until after lunch when it was still there.

'You forgot to eat your apple for lunch, Mrs Cook', said Sanjay.

Mrs Cook picked up the apple. 'No, I didn't', she said. 'I'm going to use this apple for the next lesson, in which we're going to talk about MYSELF and ask some very interesting questions'.

That got everyone's attention.

'Firstly', said Mrs Cook, 'what is an apple?'

'It's a type of fruit', said Linda.

'It's food', said Robert.

'It holds the seeds of the tree', said Sanjay.

Mrs Cook nodded. 'But, what is it made up of?'

'Skin', said someone.

'Flesh and pips'.

'Anything else?' asked the teacher.

Everyone thought for a moment.

'Smell', said Linda, 'and taste'.

To everyone's astonishment, Mrs Cook picked up a small knife and began to peel the apple. When it was done she held it up.

'Is this still an apple?' she asked.

There were nods all round.

Then she cut it into quarters and took out the pips. 'Is it still an apple?'

One or two children nodded but some weren't sure.

'How much can I take away and the remainder still be an apple?' she asked.

'It's still an apple now', said Linda.

'No, it isn't', argued Sanjay. 'How can it be an apple when it has no skin or pips? It's only part of an apple'.

The class was really divided and a lot of chatter broke out. Mrs Cook held up her hand for silence.

'What about a human being?' she asked. 'What is it?'

There was a show of hands.

'It's a person'.

'Homo something', said Robert.

'Homo Sapiens', said Mrs Cook.

'Like us'.

'And what are the parts that make up a human being', asked the teacher.

'A body', said Sanjay. Everyone giggled.

'A brain', said Linda.

'No, that's part of the body', argued Sanjay. 'There's your character'.

Mrs Cook nodded. 'The part that makes you unique. The way you react, think, behave'.

'There's your soul, too', said Linda.

'Now', said Mrs Cook. 'If you are in an accident and have a limb removed, are you still a person?'

Everyone nodded.

'What if you lose your memory so you don't know who you are or anything about your life? Are you still yourself?'

Some were doubtful about this.

'What if some wicked people changed your thoughts and beliefs by brain-washing? Are you still yourself?'

There were mixed views from the class.

'What if, because of illness or accident, your conscious brain doesn't work any more, are you still yourself?'

Few people answered. This would take some thinking about.

End

Questions

1. What question was Mrs Cook asking as she peeled and cut the apple?

2. Did the children come to a definite answer? Why not?

3. What question was Mrs Cook asking of the children, as she talked about human beings?

4. Have you ever thought about who or what you are? Would anyone like to share any ideas?

5. What did Mrs Cook mean by 'Your conscious brain'? What is consciousness? Do you think you are consciousness?

Thought for the Day:

The question 'Who am I' is one of the oldest and most difficult questions. It doesn't matter if we don't get an answer straightaway, but it is good to keep considering and asking the question.

This is a simple but powerful story which is made all the more meaningful through having the appropriate 'props' with which to demonstrate. Children readily see what are the big things in their lives, and what is less important but which sometimes takes over.

The Rocks of Life

One morning, Mr Cantwell, Year 5's form teacher, came into the classroom carrying a cardboard box, which he put down on his desk.

Children at the front craned forward to see what was in the box but Mr Cantwell didn't leave them wondering for long.

First, he took out a large jar and put it on his desk. Then he reached into the box again and took out a handful of rocks, about five centimetres in diameter, and put as many into the jar as he could.

Then he looked up at the curious faces in front of him and held up the jar.

'Would you say that this jar is full?' he asked.

There were murmurs of 'yes' and everyone nodded.

The teacher reached into the box again and took out a handful of small pebbles and poured them into the jar, shaking it so that they worked down between the rocks. He held it up again.

'Now, would you say this jar is full?' he asked.

Everyone in the class nodded and some of the children looked at each other and laughed. Now what was Mr Cantwell going to do?

He had delved into the box again, lifted out a small tin and began to pour sand into the jar. It trickled down between the rocks and the pebbles and filled up all the spaces.

'Now', said the teacher, holding up the jar for the third time. 'This jar is your life. The rocks are the important things - like your parents, your brothers and sisters, your family, your friends, your health. If you lost everything else, your life would still be full.

'The pebbles are the things that matter like school and education, later on your job, your home, your pets. The sand is everything else. The small stuff. Your CD player, your clothes, your mobile phone, TV programmes.

'If you put the sand into the jar first', went on Mr Cantwell, 'there would be no room for the pebbles or the rocks. The same goes for your life. If you spend all your time and energy on the small stuff, you will never have room for the things that are really important to you. Pay attention to the things that are really important to your happiness. Listen to your parents, have patience with your brothers and sisters, visit your grandparents. Enjoy the company of your family and appreciate your home. Be loyal and generous to your close friends. Look after your health. This is most important. Eat healthy food. You can't build strong bodies and minds with junk food.

'There will always be time to hang out with your friends, listen to CDs, play computer games and go to discos. Take care of the rocks first. The rest is just sand'.

End

Questions

1. I want you to think about the story in relation to your life - think of some rocks, some pebbles, and some sand. *(Give thinking time, then ask for examples)*.

2. Why is it that different things can be 'rocks' for different people?

3. What did the story mean by saying that the small things were not important?

4. Which are the easiest things to change? Why?

5. Would anyone ever want to change any of the big things?

6. What are some of the things you could do if you ever lost any 'rocks' in your life?

7. Can anyone sum up the meaning of the story?

Thought for the Day:

During the week, continue to see what really are the big, important things in life and those things that are less important. Do you give the most attention and time to important things or to those things that are not very important?

Who or what is the real me? This story taken from one of the Socratic dialogues continues with this difficult concept.

The Tale of the Cobbler

Over two and a half thousand years ago in Athens there lived a philosopher called Socrates. Socrates was renowned for having long conversations with his friends about the meaning of life, and how to live it better.

One day he was having a conversation with his friend, Alcibiades. They were discussing human beings, and what it meant to be a human being. Alcibiades was trying to understand what he really was. Was he his body, that others said, was handsome and strong? Perhaps he was the thoughts and ideas that were in his head? Maybe, he was spirit, but he wasn't too sure what that really was, although he and his friends often talked about it.

After a while, Socrates spoke. 'Do you remember the cobbler we saw in the market-place today?' he asked.

'Of course', said Alcibiades. 'Remember, we watched and marvelled at his skill in cutting out the leather',

'You remember the tools he was using', Socrates continued. 'Would you say that these were a part of the cobbler or separate from him?'

'I'd say they were separate from him, of course', replied Alcibiades.

'But, I was watching him closely',' Socrates went on. 'And I noticed that as he worked, he watched very carefully what he was doing, and used his hands and arms as extensions of the tools he was using. Do you agree with this my friend?'

'Yes, I see what you mean and I think that you are right - he did use his hands and arms as sorts of tools. But what do you mean by this, Socrates?'

'Well, remember you said, that the tools that our cobbler was using were not part of him, and that they were separate from him? Would you say that if he uses his arms and hands as tools then they too are separate from him and not part of what he really is? Can we say this?'

'You know, I think you're right, Socrates', said Alcibiades. 'What our cobbler really is, is behind what we can readily see. He is somehow on the inside and invisible to we who look from the outside'.

'And that is the part that I really love in you, Alcibiades', said Socrates. 'Others may love your good looks and fine physique, or perhaps your wit and intelligence, but I love that which is behind all that - the real you!'

End

Questions

1. Why did Socrates remind Alcibiades of the cobbler whom they had seen that morning?

2. Has anyone ever watched someone skillfully using tools? What did Socrates mean when he said the hands and arms were an extension of the tools?

3. Sometimes we hear of someone having to have an operation to remove part of their body. Do you think they feel the same person inside? What makes you think that - what is your evidence?

4. What was it that Socrates loved in his friend Alcibiades?

5. What is it that you love in your friends and family? Is it things on the outside or things on the inside, or both? *(Get children to explain their answers).*

Thought for the Day:

When we meet people, try to look past the things on the outside to discover what is on the inside. Connect with that.

John loved acting - using different masks and playing different characters. Through his acting, John came to learn more about himself, and to see that all of life is about playing parts. As one wise man said, 'We should learn to play our parts, and play them nicely'.

The Masks of Life

John loved acting. Whenever his school was putting on a play or concert, he was the first to volunteer.

For his seventh birthday his Gran and Grandad bought him a set of masks. There was a happy one with a smiling mouth and sparkly eyes and a sad one with a droopy mouth and tears falling from the eyes. There was an angry one with frowning eyebrows, glaring eyes and a thin, straight mouth and an excited one with a huge grin, raised eyebrows and big round eyes.

John played with them for hours. Sometimes he played the happy boy who had just been given an ice-cream and he went round being pleasant and nice to everyone and even offered a pretend lick to his baby sister, who didn't understand about pretend things and cried.

Other times he was the sad boy whose pet hamster had died and he mopped his tears with a tissue and hung his head. Then everyone was expected to pat his head and say how sorry they were.

Or, he wore the angry mask of the boy whose friends had all gone to a football match and he wasn't allowed to go. Then he stomped around, shouting and waving his fists until he frightened his little sister.

Another time, he would wear the excited mask and play the part of a boy who had just been offered a big part in a film. Then he jumped up and punched the air and laughed, hysterically.

One day, near the end of the Summer term, John came home from school, smiling.

'You look as though you have the happy mask on today, John', said Mum.

John nodded. 'I really am happy today', he said. 'Mrs Laird was really pleased with my project about the history of our town and read it out to the class'.

'Well done', said Mum.

A few days later, he came home and slumped into a chair in the kitchen and propped his chin in his hands on the table.

'Hello', said Mum. 'Today, your face looks like the sad mask'.

'I really am sad', said John. 'I'm not playing. Mrs Laird is leaving at the end of term and I really like her'.

'Never mind', said Mum. 'I'm sure your new teacher will be very nice'.

Later that evening, when John came in from visiting his friend, Rob, he went upstairs to play with his masks but soon came down again, scowling.

'Where is my angry mask?' he asked.

'You look as though you're wearing it', said Dad.

John shook his head in annoyance and stomped into the kitchen. Then he let out a shriek. When he reappeared at the living room door he was holding up the mask, in two pieces. He was breathing quickly and his eyes were cold slits.

'Look what Emily has done!' he yelled. 'She's torn my mask in two!'

'I don't think you need that mask', said Dad. 'Your face now is much angrier'.

'You shouldn't have left your mask where she could get it', said Mum.

On the last day of term, before the Summer holidays, Gran and Grandad came round. They said they had a special surprise for John.

'What is it? What is it?' asked John, jumping up and down and tugging at Gran's arm.

'Grandad and I are going to take you to Disneyland', said Gran.

John let out a whoop of joy and then laughed and punched the air.

'Ye-e-e-es!' he shouted.

'You look as though you're wearing your excited mask', said Grandad.

'I'm not playing', said John. 'I really am excited!'

The day before his trip, John was sitting quietly on his bed watching his mother pack his case. He held his masks in his hands and was looking at each one, even the angry mask, mended with sellotape.

'Who am I, really, Mum?' he asked.

His mum stopped packing and looked up.

'Remember when you were happy when your work was praised at school and then sad because your favourite teacher was leaving?'

John nodded.

'Remember how you were angry when Emily tore your mask and excited when Gran and Grandad told you about the trip to Disneyland?'

John nodded again.

'Each of these times', said Mum, 'we told you that you reminded us of your masks. You John, the real you, is Spirit, watching all that goes on. What you see are all the parts you play, the masks you have to play with. You can put any of them on at any time, in fact, you can choose which to put on and which parts to play. Happy, sad, angry, excited - anything'.

> *All the world's a stage,*
> *And all the men and women merely players;*
> *They all have their exits and their entrances,*
> *And one man in his time plays many parts . . .*
>
> *As You Like It* Act II, Scene 7 - *Shakespeare*

End

Questions

1. All of us have had times when we have felt happy or sad, excited or angry. We put on our different faces. What have you noticed that goes with a change of face? *(A change of emotion, feeling, the feeling matches the face, etc.).*

2. Why could John's Mum have said he didn't need to take his masks on holiday with him?

3. If John chose to take his 'happy face' on holiday with Gran and Grandad, what do you think the consequences would have been? See if you can get at least two. *(He would look happy, he would feel happy, probably his Gran and Grandad would feel happy, other people would be affected by his happiness).*

4. What do you think the first two lines of the quotation from Shakespeare mean?

Thought for the Day:

See if you can notice what sorts of masks you put on today, and also see how you feel at that time.

TRUTH

Telling the truth is perhaps the first connection with truth that children come across, and this, although simple, is of paramount importance. Children must see that telling the truth is of great importance - it will have a great effect on their lives in gross and subtle ways. Connected with this is the understanding that truth and untruth have consequences.

Secondly, and also important, is holding to what is known to be true, or to one's principles - 'To thine own self be true, and it must follow, as the night the day, thou can not then be false to any man'.

Another aspect of truth is knowing the truth about a situation. If we do not have true knowledge we make poor decisions and actions, because they are based on ignorance. Consider the old Indian story of the man who thought he saw a snake in his house. He took action accordingly, but when someone switched the light on he saw that the snake was in fact a coil of rope, which led to entirely different actions. It behoves us to try to see the true knowledge that is in every situation.

In a philosophical sense, 'Truth' is connected with 'Being', it is what one may become through the accumulation and exemplification of other virtues such as patience, goodness, wisdom and so on. Although in a sense one may become it, Truth is an entirely natural state - it is what we are if we can get rid of what we are not! Rather like peeling away the layers of the onion, Truth is waiting to be discovered!

This short play offers two scenarios to the same situation - one where someone tells lies and inevitably makes a situation worse for herself, and another where she tells the truth, which although not without repercussions, is an end to the situation.

A Tangled Web

'Oh what a tangled web we weave when first we practice to deceive . . . '
Shakespeare

Cast: Narrator, Teacher, Tim, Elizabeth, Sue.

Narrator: It was break time at Wellington Street Primary. A warm, spring morning when everyone was outside. In fact, no-one was allowed in the classrooms during break.

Elizabeth Edison made sure no-one was watching as she sneaked into school. In the classroom she hurried around the tables where the class had been doing painting. Her skirt brushed a large piece of paper which in turn knocked over a pot of green paint. It splattered everywhere, ruining some of the artwork and spilt over someone's schoolbag.

Elizabeth turned and ran out of the room.

TELLING LIES ■

Teacher: 'Who has been into the classroom and spilt this paint?'

Tim: 'I saw Elizabeth come into school'.

Teacher: 'Did you come into school, Elizabeth?'

Elizabeth: 'No, Mrs Foster'.

Teacher: 'How did you get that green paint on your skirt?'

Elizabeth: *(looking down at her skirt)* 'My Dad was painting a chair this morning'.

Tim: 'You said your Dad was away in America'.

173

Elizabeth:	'It was my Mum painting the chair'.
Teacher:	'Painting a chair bright green?'
Elizabeth:	'It's a garden chair'.
Sue:	You haven't got a garden. You live in a flat, like us'.
Elizabeth:	'It's my grandparents' chair. They have a garden'.
Tim:	'But your grandparents live a long way away. What was their garden chair doing in your house?'
Elizabeth:	'I was at my grandparents' house'.
Teacher:	'What? In your school uniform?'

TELLING THE TRUTH ■■■■■■■■■■■■■■■■■■■■■■■■■■■■■■

Teacher:	'Who has been into the classroom and spilt this paint?'
Tim:	'I saw Elizabeth come into school'.
Teacher:	'Did you come into school, Elizabeth?'
Elizabeth:	*(looking worried)* 'Yes, Mrs Foster. I'm sorry. I accidentally knocked the paint over'.
Teacher:	'Why didn't you come and tell someone straight away?'
Elizabeth:	'I was scared of getting into trouble. I wasn't supposed to be in the classroom, anyway'.
Teacher:	'Why were you in here during break?'
Elizabeth:	'I was going to play a trick on Tim because he was teasing me this morning'.
Teacher:	'Silly girl! Now, go and get a mop and clear this mess up'.
Narrator:	Elizabeth fetches a mop and bucket and mops up the mess amid teasing and laughter from her classmates. Then she tried to wash out the stain on her skirt but it wouldn't come out. Her mum would be cross. It was a new skirt this term.

Sue: 'Look at my school bag! It's ruined. You'll have to pay for a new one, Elizabeth. It's a good thing it was closed so none got inside'.

Tim: 'That'll teach you not to play tricks on people'.

End

Questions

1. Who can remember a time when they told a lie? What was the result?

2. Shakespeare said, 'Oh what a tangled web we weave when first we practice to deceive'. What do you think it means? Do you think it is true?

3. When Elizabeth told the truth in the second story, was she let off or were there still consequences? *(If yes)* What were they?

4. What was the difference for Elizabeth between the time she told the truth and the time she didn't? What would be the consequences in the first situation and what would be the consequences in the second?

5. Is it always easy to tell the truth? Why? Why not?

6. Why does it seem easy to sometimes tell a lie? Has anyone an example? What happens in the long run if we do this?

Thought for the Day:

Telling the truth is not always easy, but it is important. If you have done something wrong and tell the truth, you may have to face the consequences but at least then it is finished - it doesn't go on and on.

One of the aspects of Truth is keeping to one's principles. Kay wanted a nice fleece that she had spotted, but knew that she didn't have the money for it. As we've all felt, Kay felt the pull of emotional desire to have the fleece begin to make her question her principles.

Window Shopping

During the school holidays Kay usually went to stay with her Auntie Doris as her mum worked and couldn't always get the time off. Kay didn't mind at all. There was always plenty to do in the city and Auntie Doris was a real fun person to be with. She told endless stories about what she and Kay's mum, her sister, had got up to when they were girls.

'Let's go into town today', said Auntie Doris, on the second day of the autumn half term. 'Maybe we can get some Christmas shopping done'.

They parked the car, and had no sooner stepped out into the shopping mall when Kay saw the fleece in the window. It was so lovely it stopped her in her tracks.

'That is so cool', she whispered. 'Wow! Would I love to buy that!'

'I don't know about cool', said Auntie Doris, with a grin, 'it looks really warm and cosy to me'.

Kay laughed and nudged her aunt. 'You know what I mean'.

'A bit expensive', said Auntie Doris. 'But if you really like it why not see if they've got your size? Have you got enough money?'

Kay thought. Since she was ten, two years ago, her mum had let her have control of her child allowance. Out of that monthly sum she had to buy all her clothes, sweets and snacks, presents, cinema tickets, in fact . . . everything. Kay enjoyed budgeting and looking for things in sales. She felt really pleased when she came away with a bargain. She was determined to handle her money wisely and never to borrow. She really felt strongly about that.

But this beautiful arctic fleece was no bargain. It would take more than her monthly allowance - and there was Christmas coming up. In fact, she didn't have enough money, and told her aunt so.

'Well', said Auntie Doris. 'I know you're good with money so I'll lend it to you if you like. You can pay me back in the New Year'.

Kay continued to stare at the fleece. She could see how soft the material was - and the colour just took her breath away. A sort of very pale turquoise with white lining. The designer name was embroidered very discreetly on the front in white silk.

No-one else would have a fleece like this. Kay thought about the admiring comments her friends would make. She would really feel good wearing it. It would be worth the money. Auntie Doris was happy to lend her the money so she could still do her Christmas shopping and survive for the rest of the month.

'I'll just go and try it on', she said, walking towards the shop door and half hoping that they wouldn't have her size.

But they did. And it fitted and felt wonderful. Kay turned this way and that in front of the mirror in the changing room. Really cool! It looked so good with her black jeans.

But it was a lot of money. More than she'd ever spent on anything before. And how she hated borrowing. For over two months she would be in debt. Even then, she would be really skint when she needed the money most, what with Christmas presents and parties.

It did look good, though.

'Hurry up in there!' called Auntie Doris. 'Make up your mind'.

It would last next winter as well, wouldn't it? That is, if she didn't grow too much.

But would it still be fashionable? She might have grown tired of it and it would certainly have lost its impact on her friends. Something that expensive needed to be worn a lot to get your money's worth, especially borrowed money.

Kay took off the fleece. She fondled the soft material, longingly, put on her own jacket, and went out of the changing rooms, back into the shop. Then she placed it onto the counter.

'No thanks', she said to the assistant, 'I can't afford it'.

Kay walked out of the shop without looking back at the fleece in the window. She felt relieved. She had stuck to her principles. What she couldn't afford, she couldn't have. She was not going to start borrowing. It was a bad habit that would stick.

'Come on, Auntie Doris', she said, happily. 'Shopping and then lunch!'

End

'This above all:
To thine own self be true,
And it must follow, as the night the day,
Thou can not then be false to any man . . . '
Hamlet Act 1 Sc.3

Shakespeare

Questions

1. Have you ever had something that you really wanted but couldn't afford? Why did you want it? What did you do about it?

2. Why did Kay want the fleece? Why didn't she buy it?

3. What might have been the consequences if Kay had bought the fleece?

4. The story says Kay had stuck to her principles. What does this mean? What was this particular principle?

5. Can you think of any principles that you have? Do you keep to them? Why do you keep to them?

6. What kinds of things sometimes try to make you not keep to your principles?

Thought for the Day:

Sometimes we say that people who keep to their principles are honourable. It means they keep their word and can be trusted. They do what they say they will do. This is a good thing for everyone. Try to always keep to your word.

Someone who shows the Truth in their life, really reflects the virtues (as in this book) through their actions. These include, for example, happiness, patience, knowledge and goodness. In this story, these qualities are shown by Barry the St. Bernard. Although some may argue that a dog cannot show Truth, through the example, children can see that they can consciously choose to show these qualities and so live in Truth. It is a difficult but worthwhile concept for children to begin to understand.

The Snow Dog

Barry whined again and scratched at the door. At last, a man approached across the stone floor and opened it. The wind flung in a swirl of snowflakes as the big St Bernard bounded out into the dark, cold night. He knew something was wrong. There had been an avalanche and someone was trapped.

Barry loped through the deep snow, his thick fur protecting him from the cold. Now and again he raised his face into the wind to get the scent.

Here was the place. Fresh snow, piled high. He began to dig.

Soon, hooded figures arrived, their lamps swinging, casting a glow onto the white snow. They had brought shovels and they began to dig, too.

'Here he is!' shouted one, at last, and the others held their lamps high while the man was uncovered. 'He's alive!'

Barry licked the man's frozen face with his warm tongue and then the monks helped the man to his feet.

'You saved my life', said the man, but the monks shook their heads.

'No, it was Barry here who saved your life. He knew someone was in trouble'.

The man turned to Barry and patted his head in gratitude. Barry wagged his tail and licked the man's hand.

'Come', said one of the monks. 'There is a hot meal and a warm bed waiting for you in the hospice'.

High in the Alps between Switzerland and Italy is the great St Bernard Pass. It is here that the 'Snow Dogs', or St Bernards, as we now know them, were first used to guide and rescue travellers lost in blizzards or fog or buried underneath avalanches.

At an altitude of 2,500 metres, the pass is covered with snow for nine months of the year. A hospice has stood at the top since the middle of the 11th Century and the monks there have offered refuge and shelter to the many thousands who traversed the mountains on foot and risked death from cold, hunger and avalanche. They received a warm welcome, a bed for the night and a meal, all free of charge. This was no small task. For the year 1817, for example, it is recorded that 34,863 meals were provided for around 20,000 people.

The first mention of St Bernard dogs was around 1708, although they weren't called that then. The dogs were originally kept as companions because of their gentle temperament, but the monks soon discovered that they had a remarkable ability to find people lost in the mountains or buried under the snow, in fact they could predict snow storms or avalanches. They also had an amazing sense of direction.

Each morning, one of the monks accompanied by a St Bernard would go to meet the travellers with bread, cheese and wine. Thick fog can suddenly descend in the mountains, or raging blizzards appear from nowhere.

Barry was one of these dogs *(his name meant 'little bear')*. He was born in 1800 and during his twelve years of service rescued over forty people. He showed great patience and would never give up, even when he was exhausted. When Barry grew too old to work he was retired and went to live in Berne, where he died two years later. His body was preserved and can still be seen in the Natural History Museum there.

These days, there is a tunnel under the St Bernard Pass as the road over the top is only open from June to September. The dogs are still there during that time, although only as a tourist attraction. Barry is still there too, but another Barry, in fact each year the best male dog is named after his famous ancestor.
Many people visit the kennels and are reminded of the great bravery and devotion of the Snow Dogs.

End

Questions

1. How did Barry know there had been an avalanche?

2. Was Barry 'being good' in saving the man? Why did he do it?

3. Why was he pleased when the man was revived? Did he actually know he had saved a life?

4. Barry was patient, and would keep digging even when he was exhausted. What made him like that?

5. Some people say that living the Truth is when we show good qualities like Barry - patience, service, goodness, knowledge. Do you think we are just born like that, or can we choose to be like that? What is your evidence?

6. Do you know someone with some of these qualities? What does it feel like to be with them?

Thought for the Day:

We have a choice as to whether we want to show good qualities and live in Truth. When you find you are being patient, serving someone or being good to people, be awake to see how this affects others.

Henri Dunant was true to his idea or cause in bringing the Red Cross to fruition. In the process he reflected Truth by showing that our humanity is about seeing the unity between us, and striving to serve that, no matter what the nationality of the people.

The Red Cross

The weather was stifling hot and the man on horseback longed to reach his destination and enjoy a cool drink and shelter from the sun.

He rode along the dusty road, just under the brow of a hill, from time to time hearing noises from far away. A horse whinny, men shouting, the clank of metal. It was the bugle that made him get off his horse and climb the ridge to look over onto the plain below. The man gasped, with shock. Huge armies were amassing there, thousands and thousands of men, some on horseback, some on foot with bayoneted rifles, some walking beside cannon pulled by horses, some in armour glinting in the sun.

As he watched, the bugle sounded the charge, the drums rolled and the two sides merged in violent combat, the French and Italians on one side and the Austrians on the other.

The man was a Swiss called Henri Dunant. He was a rich businessman on his way to speak to the French Emperor about a brilliant business plan he had devised. He had meant to see the emperor at his headquarters here in Italy. But he had obviously come at a bad time.

For fifteen hours the battle raged while Henri watched from his hilltop, appalled, yet unable to leave.

The Austrians, in their white coats, yellow and black battle flags flying, bombarded the French with artillery from their standpoint in the hills. Hails of shells thundered into the ground throwing up soil and clouds of dust.

Soon, the vast battleground was littered with dead and wounded soldiers. Rifles cracked, cannon boomed, yet, above it all, Henri could hear the cries of the wounded and the whinny of horses. Acrid smoke reached his nostrils and made him cough. He watched canteen women moving among the wounded, giving them water and risking their own lives.

In the midst of the battle a whirlwind blew up and his view was completely blocked by the swirling dust. Then rain and hail thundered down. The sky grew dark and flashes of lightning lit up that terrible scene down on the plain.

When at last it was over, Henri trudged to the nearest village to be met with a terrible sight. Hundreds of wounded soldiers were also making their way there, uniforms torn and bloody. Some were on stretchers and others were helped by their comrades.

It was at that moment that Henri's life changed.

For three days he stayed in the village, burying the dead, comforting the dying, sometimes helping them to write a last letter to their parents. Occasionally, he helped the few doctors in any way he could but the situation was impossible. The year was 1859 and the battle he had witnessed was the Battle of Solferino. In it, 300,000 men took part and 40,000 of them were killed or injured. What could so few people do to help?

When, at last, Henri arrived back home in Geneva he wrote a book about the battle, about efforts to care for the wounded afterwards, and about a plan he had. The plan was that nations of the world should form societies and train volunteers to care for the wounded in times of war. These people should be guaranteed neutrality by displaying an emblem on their vehicles - a red cross on a white background, which is the Swiss flag, in reverse.

Sixteen countries approved the plan and so the 'Red Cross' was formed. Later its work was extended to help people after natural catastrophes such as famine or earthquake.

While Henri was busy with this worthwhile cause, he neglected his business and his big plan failed. This meant that he not only lost all his money, but all the money of his friends whom he had urged to invest in it. He was so disliked that he had to leave Geneva and went to live in a little village called Heiden.

For twenty years the world forgot about Henri Dunant and then he became ill and was moved to a hospice. There, a local school teacher found out where he was and told the world. Henri Dunant once again became a celebrity and was the first person to be awarded the Nobel Peace Prize.

He stayed in the hospice for eighteen years, until his death in 1910, when he was buried without a funeral or mourners. In accordance with his wishes, he was carried to his grave 'like a dog'.

In Muslim countries the emblem is the red crescent and in Iran it is the red lion and sun.

End

Questions

1. Why did Henri put aside his first idea? *(The one that he was going to tell to the Emperor).*

2. What was the cause of his second idea? *(The one about forming societies to care for people in war).*

3. Henri was true to his idea of forming the Red Cross, but what was the consequence on his business idea?

4. Do you have any evidence as to the kind of person Henri was, and if so what is it?

5. Why did Henri's friends and business partners dislike him? Was that fair? Why or why not?

6. What do you think a true person is? Was Henri Dunant one?

Thought for the Day:

Henri Dunant was true to his cause, and worked hard to start the Red Cross. He also showed he was a true person by the way he had feelings for others and tried to help them. We can all try to be reliable people to others and show that we are true friends.

Harley's friendship with Elliot is tested to the limit as he sees his friend accused of sabotaging the school trip. However, being a true friend, Harley supports Elliot and trusts in him.

Friends

'I'm hungry', whispered Harley. 'Starving, I cant wait until breakfast'.

The other boy in the tent sighed. 'I feel sick', he said. 'I'm dreading tomorrow'.

'Give it a rest, Elliot!' said Harley. 'Everyone on this whole trip knows you're dreading the abseiling tomorrow'.

Elliot didn't answer but Harley could hear him tossing and turning inside his sleeping bag.

The next morning, the whole camp was buzzing with excitement. It was the first full day on their adventure holiday and everyone - except Elliot - was looking forward to the abseiling.

Harley pulled on his jeans and tee shirt. Elliot wasn't there. Maybe he couldn't sleep and had gone for a walk. He felt sorry for his friend now. Being scared was awful. They were all a bit scared but he knew that Elliot was terrified. No-one would force him to do the abseiling but he'd be teased, no end, if he chickened out.

He opened the tent flap and went outside. At that moment the babble of chatter died down and Harley followed everyone's gaze. Their chief instructor, Mr Johnson, was leading Elliot in front of him. Elliot looked utterly miserable and Mr Johnson was holding something in his hand. He held it up for all to see. It was the abseiling ropes, and they were cut to pieces.

'Elliot here', he said, 'did not want to do any abseiling, so he has made sure no-one else does, either. I just caught him with the ropes in his hands and a penknife in his pocket'.

Harley watched, in dismay, as the boys went wild, yelling like a lynch mob. Mr Johnson had a job keeping them off Elliot, who said nothing in his defence but just cowered away.

'You're off home, lad', said Mr Johnson, 'just as soon as we can call your parents to come and fetch you. In the meantime, we'll do some canoeing today, instead. I'll phone the sports shop later and we might be able to get some more ropes'.

After breakfast, they all trooped down to the edge of the lake, Harley staying at the back with Elliot. He made sure they shared a canoe and that they stayed well away from any of the others. Although their initial anger had cooled a little, he didn't fancy he and Elliot's canoe being overturned unexpectedly. He was growing tired of the taunts and name-calling, too.

Elliot hadn't done it, Harley was sure. He would never sabotage something like that. He didn't have to abseil and had wanted to overcome his fear. There must be some other explanation but he knew better than to question his friend. He was sure that Elliot would tell him later.

But he didn't. They hardly spoke to each other all morning and no-one spoke to them. What a fun trip this was turning out to be, thought Harley.

At lunchtime, Elliot crept away and sat at the edge of the clearing while the others tucked, hungrily, into a packed lunch.

'Can I get you something?' asked Harley, walking over to him. Elliot just shook his head.

'Come on, you must be starving'.

'I'll live', said Elliot.

Later that afternoon, when they got back to camp, something else happened. Some crisps and biscuits were missing from the food stores and all eyes turned to Elliot as the obvious thief. After all, he had gone without lunch.

'Did you take them, Elliot?' asked Mr Johnson.

'Course he did!' yelled one boy. 'He's a thief as well as a coward!'

Other voices rose to agree.

'Tell them it wasn't you', urged Harley.

Elliot looked up at him. 'How do you know it wasn't?'

'It wouldn't be like you', said Harley. 'Only I wish you would tell me what really happened'.

'I can't', replied Elliot.

Why can't he, thought Harley. If he's innocent he should say so. For a moment, even he had a little doubt in his mind but then he swept it away. Elliot was definitely not guilty.

Soon, the camp fire was blazing and everyone joined in the cooking. Things tasted far better cooked in the open over a fire than at home. They all ate with hearty appetites. Elliot too, ate something, although it was Harley who cooked his food and took it to him.

When the food was gone and the songs and story-telling began, Elliot slunk away back to their tent and Harley went with him.

'You don't have to spoil your fun too', said Elliot.

Harley shrugged. 'We came together, we'll stick together'. As he said it he wondered what he would do when Elliot's parents came for him. Would he go back too or would he stay and enjoy the rest of the holiday? He finally went to sleep, still undecided.

A lot of shouting woke them up and before they could struggle into their clothes, the siren of a police car grew louder and they could see the flashing lights through the tent wall.

Emerging into the sunlight, they were in time to see two youths being led away by the police and put into the police car. Out of the corner of his eye, Harley saw Elliot's face relax for the first time in two days.

Then, Mr Johnson was walking towards them, smiling, awkwardly.

'Elliot', he said. 'I owe you an apology. Why didn't you tell me?'

'They threatened me, Sir', said Elliot. 'I found them cutting the ropes and they threatened me, if I told. They had a knife'.

Mr Johnson nodded, grimly, and patted Elliot's shoulder. 'I found them trying to sabotage our canoes this morning', he said. 'It was such a lovely morning I got up early and went down to the lake and there they were. I phoned the police on my mobile before I confronted them'.

Harley grinned at his friend. 'I knew you were innocent'.

'Thanks', said Elliot. 'It really looked as though I'd done it, I know, and I wanted to explain to you, but I daren't. You would have had to tell Mr Johnson'.

Harley turned to their instructor. 'Why did those boys do that?'

Mr Johnson shrugged. 'Some people don't need a reason. Maybe they were envious of the fun we were having'.

'Talking of fun, what are we doing today, Sir?'

Mr Johnson grinned. 'Some new ropes are arriving this morning. I thought we'd go abseiling'.

Elliot's face went pale but then he laughed. 'Can I go first please? Then I'll get it over with and can enjoy watching everyone else'.

End

Questions

1. Even though the evidence was against Elliot for having cut the ropes, Harley didn't believe his friend had done it. Did he have any evidence for this?

2. Were there any other reasons for Harley's belief?

3. Sometimes, we talk about a 'true friend'. What do you think makes a true friend?

4. Was Harley a true friend? Why?

5. Elliot knew the truth about the slashed ropes, but was too scared to tell. Did that mean he wasn't truthful?

6. How do you think the others felt when it was shown that Elliot was not responsible for the damage? Did they have reasonable evidence for their opinions?

Thought for the Day:

Consider whether you have any true friends, or whether you are a true friend to anybody. This means trusting each other, looking after each other, and standing up for each other – even when things get tough, as they did for Elliot. Having a true friend is a very valuable thing.

Appendix 'A'

Examples of various types of questions that help to extend and develop thinking. They seek alternative views, test implications, seek clarification, probe for reasons and evidence and on occasion provide a *'scaffold'* to further the thinking processes. The list is to provide ideas and is certainly not exhaustive.

Can you explain that?

What do you mean by?

Can you put it another way?

Who has another point of view?

Why do you think that?

What are your reasons?

Do you have evidence?

What would be the consequence?

How could we test that?

Who can summarise so far?

What is the cause of that?

How can we tell if that's true?

What is the reason for?

If . . . . then what do you think about?

What makes you think that?